COUNSELLING
IN DISABILITY
AND ILLNESS

COUNSELLING IN DISABILITY AND ILLNESS

2nd Edition

GILL BREARLEY

MCSP, Cert.Ed., Dip. Counselling

and

PETER BIRCHLEY

CQSW, CSW,

Cert. Family Casework and Law

M Mosby

Publisher:	Griselda Campbell
Project Manager:	Alison Taylor
Production:	Hilary Scott
Index:	Susan Ramsey
Design:	Judith Gauge
Cover Design:	Lara Last

Copyright © 1994 Times Mirror International Publishers Limited.
Published in 1994 by Mosby, an imprint of Times Mirror International Publishers Limited.

First edition published as Introducing Counselling Skills and Techniques in 1986 by Faber and Faber Limited. Reprinted in 1992 by Wolfe Publishing, an imprint of Times Mirror International Publishers.

Printed and bound in Great Britain by Biddles Ltd, Guildford and King's Lynn.

ISBN 0 7234 19760

A CIP catalogue record for this book is available from the British Library.

For full details of all Times Mirror International Publishers Limited titles please write to Times Mirror International Publishers Limited, Lynton House, 7–12 Tavistock Square, London WC1H 9LB, England.

TO OUR CO-COUNSELLORS

CONTENTS

THE BOOK

In 1979 the authors led their first course 'introducing counselling skills' to people with disabilities. This course was designed to provide an opportunity to explore and practice counselling skills for people who could not, for reasons of access or communication, easily attend the regular courses.

Over several years, the initial format gradually altered to include able-bodied participants with interest in the field of disability. At first, these students were those accompanying students with disability as helpers, but the courses developed into being open to anyone wishing to explore the special counselling needs of people with illness or disability.

These courses, and others for special groups of particular professions and interests, have included physiotherapists, social workers, speech and language therapists, occupational therapists, teachers, care workers and partners and parents of people with disabilities.

All expressed an urgent need for knowledge of the counselling skills needed when working with their particular patient or client group.

When the authors started their series of courses there were few counsellors who felt able, for whatever reason, to accept people with disability onto their case load.

It is our experience that this has not altered to any significant degree.

This book is an attempt to present a 'workshop' in counselling skills, with special reference to illness and disability, for all those working in this field among the paramedical professions and beyond. We believe that if you are aware of the patient/client's need for counselling and if you are asked for help, you can discover and develop the skills necessary for you to be able to respond.

We believe that you *will* be asked. Reading this book could be the start of equipping yourself to respond to that request.

Jargon is used by groups as a form of shorthand and sometimes as a way of excluding those outside that group. We have tried to avoid the use of jargon in this book. When we have felt it essential to use words which have a specific and possibly idiosyncratic meaning within their context we have defined the word in the text. A glossary is provided to enable the reader to make rapid reference.

Throughout the text, the patient/client is referred to as 'he' except when case studies are quoted. Similarly, the counsellor and other helpers are referred to as 'she'. This is solely for convenience and clarity and is in no way intended to imply any form of sexual stereotyping.

When case studies are quoted it is with the permission of those concerned. Names used are fictitious. In all cases the scripts have been edited for publication so that they read more fluently.

Using the book

Read from beginning to end, the book suggests to the reader the need for counselling in the particular areas of illness and disability, describes some basic techniques, the skills required and the support that will be needed for the counsellor. Specific areas of client need and alternative approaches are described while a bibliography and list of useful organisations end the book.

All topics covered are particularly related to the needs of clients with illness or disability.

Readers with experience of counselling may wish to refer to chapters specific to particular topics and the authors have endeavoured to make each chapter complete in itself with cross-references when appropriate.

PREFACE

FACING DRAGONS

In mythology and folklore, dragons are creatures of immense power and mysterious knowledge. Carl Jung describes the dragon as traditionally a personification of the cosmic powers of evil (Man and His Symbols, Carl Jung 1964). The association of the dragon with overwhelming power and evil has resulted in the dragon becoming a common symbol for powerful negative emotions: anger, greed and rapaciousness, lust.

The hero of folklore sets out to conquer the dragon, which is terrorising the country and devouring maidens. He must first of all find his enemy; dragons traditionally live in hidden caves where they guard vast stores of stolen treasure. A perilous journey is often involved. Magical help is frequently available, often acquired through helping an apparently poor and derelict person.

He must be suitably armed. St George challenged his dragon protected by a suit of armour, mounted on a charger, and with a sword and shield. Other heroes have conquered their dragons with the help of special knowledge of the dragon's vulnerable points or with magic potions or protection. These last methods would seem to involve less risk to the hero!

The dragon vanquished, the hero is richly rewarded. He has won the dragon's hoard of treasure. He may marry the rescued princess, receive gold or become king. In some accounts he also acquires the dragon's wisdom and strength.

There are dragons facing all of us. Unrecognised grief and anger, guilt and fears, unresolved emotions that lurk in the dark caves of our unconscious or rage destructively through our lives. These dragons can affect the way we live and relate to others to varying degrees. We may not recognise their powers or may be in such terror of them that we hide ourselves and deny their existence.

Counselling is about helping people recognise and name their dragons, face them and win their strength and treasures.

GLOSSARY

Block An unrecognised or unacknowledged action or course of behaviour that prevents a person from pursuing a desired or desirable course of action, or prevents a counsellor from recognising a client's feelings when these too closely approximate to her own.

Body image The picture a person forms in his mind that represents his impression of his physical appearance and attributes. His behaviour will conform to this impression.

Client One who asks for and receives counselling.

Client-centred therapy A model of counselling which holds that a client is the only person who can define his own problems and find the appropriate solutions or resolutions with the help of the counsellor.

Conditioned response A pattern of behaviour produced as a result of external demands and established by the approval of parenting people.

Congruence The counsellor's awareness of her own feelings in the counselling relationship and the sharing of such feelings and emotions with the client where appropriate.

Cop-out A rationalised response, not always consciously recognised, that absolves a person from perceiving and responding to the real needs of another or of recognising her real motives.

Counselling The use of skills that enable a client to recognise and identify his own problems, and the ability to help the client find his own solution or resolution.

Denial A conscious or subconscious refusal, or inability, to recognise and/or acknowledge a painful or unpleasant fact.

Empathy The deliberate attempt to share another person's experiences, and experience the world as he perceives it.

Euphoria An appearance of well-being that may be at variance with the facts of a situation and not based in reality.

Fantasy A person's interpretation of what he perceives as reality, based on his own assumptions.

Gestalt Wholeness, a balanced entirety of personality.

Investment The committal of trust or emotional expression to another person, or the committal of emotional fulfilment to a particular course of action.

Identification The recognition of aspects of oneself in another person, or the adoption of thought processes, mannerisms, etc. of an admired person.

Libido Sexual urge.

Reflecting Repeating to a client in his own words, or an equivalent form, a thought or feeling he has expressed. This can enable a client to recognise his true feelings and indicates acceptance by the counsellor.

Repression Relegating to the unconscious unacceptable or painful experiences or thoughts.

Resolution A strategy or course of action enabling a person to live an acceptable life with a problem that may be intractable and incapable of solution.

Role-play The player is in possession of a few facts about the person whose role he is to play. He then uses those facts and his own feelings to experience and share with a partner or group the real and deep feelings that are aroused. Role-play is not acting or pretending, but an exploration of the genuine feelings that situations can arouse.

Solution The answer to and dismissal of a problem.

Strategy A course of behaviour or action designed consciously or unconsciously to achieve a desired result.

Sub-verbal counselling Enabling the client to recognise and resolve feelings and problems using indirect means.

Supervisor A counselling colleague with whom a counsellor can work to assess and evaluate her own work with a client, and to resolve her own feelings and difficulties that may be aroused when working with a client.

Transactional Analysis A model of the personality that recognises a number of ego-states existing in the adult which influence his relationships and decisions.

PROLOGUE

BEN— A PERSON IN NEED OF HELP

Ben glanced up at the kitchen clock. Half an hour before the children arrived home from school — time for a quiet cup of coffee. He reached for his elbow crutches, levered himself forward and pushed himself upright.

As he filled the kettle, Ben wondered fleetingly if the tremor in his hands was getting worse. Then, remembering yesterday's appointment at the neurological clinic, he grinned wryly at his overactive imagination. Nobody whose multiple sclerosis (MS) was in regression would have got through the housework he had coped with today.

Ben slid the cup of coffee along the work surface and made his way back to his chair. He reflected that it had been a good day. Jean was going to get something for supper on her way home. They were still feeling excited at her luck in getting such a plum job after not working for 10 years. She enjoyed it so much and it meant a great deal to Jean that she was able to relieve Ben's mind of financial worry.

Nowadays, he knew, there was no stigma attached to the man playing the role of housewife. It was, in any case, infinitely preferable to the humiliating offer of a job operating a lift. This offer had been made, so kindly, by the head office of his newspaper. Ben's appointment as foreign correspondent had coincided with the onset of the condition so cosily referred to as MS.

He imagined for a moment what it would have been like, had he accepted the offer. From world-wide investigator to lift-boy, his travels suddenly narrowed to the confines of a grimy lift, his glittering scoops reduced to half-heard snippets of news and other people's second-hand preoccupations.

Ben reached for the comfort of his coffee, with a glance at the pile of ironing that had been today's major achievement. Better to be grateful for such achievements than to indulge himself in painful harking back. There had never been time for the luxury of a peaceful cup of coffee in those days.

He looked at the clock again. Jean should by now have collected the car. No problems with the MOT test, but then there ought not to be. It was a solid, reliable, if unexciting, model. They had been lucky that his successor had coveted Ben's own car enough to give them a good price.

Jean knew how to look after a car, too. So Ben had no excuse to worry on that score. She was a wonderful person.

Jean was a down-to-earth woman who took everything in her stride. She had taken the news of his illness so calmly and had quietly and tactfully taken over. There was never any question or fuss about it. There didn't even seem to be any need to talk about it. A capable person, Ben mused. Capable of managing on her own even if he wasn't there. Perhaps better, without the frustration of watching him fumble through jobs she could do in half the time.

Ben shook himself mentally, he was sliding into self-pity again. He felt a twinge of shame — the same feelings he experienced when he attended his weekly classes at the physiotherapy department. There, he saw so many people in worse situations than his own. There was such an infectiously optimistic feel about the place and everyone seemed to respond to it. Why, then, did he always leave feeling let down and irritable?

Even the children there seemed to catch the cheerful atmosphere. A group of children with cerebral palsy, almost babies, who to Ben were shockingly deformed, responded so readily to all that was asked of them. All the experiences Ben had enjoyed as a child and young man were denied them. How could he feel sorry for himself in the face of these children? How could he feel sorry for himself when so many people were using their skills to help him? He couldn't fault the doctors, the physios were marvellous and the occupational therapists and social workers were a mine of practical information.

Even the other patients put him to shame. Ben remembered the young man, almost totally paralysed after a motor cycle accident, who exchanged banter and teasing with the porters, physios and other patients until the whole gym was in an uproar.

Ben had wanted to talk about that to his social worker, wanting to know what would happen to the young man when he was discharged from hospital. Where did such people go, people who could not look after themselves, whose families could not be expected to cope with the physical care needed? Unfortunately, although the social worker, who was a most reliable and helpful young woman, had called this week she was obviously harassed. She was very pleasant, but Ben had the impression that all her other cases needed far more of her time than he could legitimately claim. She had a family to care for as well, her husband was not disabled so she had the household chores to cope with when she got home; at least Jean was spared that.

He felt he could not take up her time with his irrelevancies, so he had simply repeated his thanks for the entry-phone and confirmed that it was fixed and working. He really was grateful for that gadget. The kids loved it too, and would soon be shouting into the microphone and waiting for the 'magic' unlocking of the door by the remote control switch. Fun for the kids, but a real boon for Ben. He remembered too many laborious journeys to the front door only to find an impatient caller had already gone.

The doorbell rang. Ben smiled, pressed the button conveniently close at hand and the voice of his son, with nine-year-old dignity, announced his arrival home. Ben could hear the complaints of his daughter as she tried to push her elder brother aside. Susan had been all assertion from the moment she was born, whereas Tim had been self-contained even as a tiny baby. Ben had had so many plans for all the things he was going to share with them. That, or course, had been when he was fit.

As the door opened, Ben heard Jean's car draw up.

1.

THE COUNSELLOR — WHO IS SHE?

It has been suggested that skilled help may be needed in some circumstances. The term 'counsellor' has been used. We would suggest that skills involved in enabling distressed people to recognise their feelings, to define their problems, and in helping people to find their own solutions or to begin to resolve their dilemmas, are skills that can be developed by many people if they are willing to do so. These skills are those of the counsellor.

The definition of counselling used here is based on the concept of client-centred therapy. This concept embodies the belief that the client is the only person who can ultimately define his particular problems, and the only person who can recognise the solution or resolution appropriate to himself. In this context, we would define 'solution' as a course of action leading to the overcoming of a problem or its disappearance, and 'resolution' as a strategy or action enabling the client to live a life of a quality acceptable to himself when the problem is irresolvable.

If a client feels that a particular person will accept his confidences, give permission for shared feelings, is someone in whom trust can be invested, he may ask that person for help.

This request will seldom, if ever, be direct unless the client is making an appointment with a recognised counsellor. It will be important for the asker to be assured that the acceptance is really there and that the request for help is appropriate. Most of us fear rejection, judgement, ridicule or condemnation and will, in consequence, negotiate carefully and cautiously.

DARING TO RESPOND

We suggest that the client will present the counsellor with signals which will indicate a need for counselling. We shall look at some possible responses. These signals may be verbal, and we shall enlarge on how a client may ask for counselling help, although often there are other signals which are also clear to those aware that help is requested.

A patient may, for example, respond to an enquiry with the words 'I'm fine'. At the same time a sideways glance may query whether this statement is believed or an averted gaze may indicate a dishonest statement. A 'closed' body position, with arms crossed, shoulders hunched and head low, can clearly indicate a lack of openness in verbal communication. Similarly, a response from the counsellor given with a direct glance making eye contact with the client and an open receptive body position will indicate a genuinely caring attitude.

Very often, though, no response is made. Although the signal has been received it is neither acknowledged nor acted upon. We suspect that many of us have found ourselves in the position of being ignored in this way at some time. Equally, we could all put forward some very good reasons why we have failed to respond to another's need.

If these reasons are carefully examined and we are able to be honest with ourselves, we shall see that they often stem from fear of one sort or another. Perhaps it is necessary to emphasise here that fear is a natural phenomenon and entirely to be expected. Many of us have been conditioned throughout our lives either to repress our fears or try to ignore them. Neither of these methods is very effective as a long-term measure. Our own fears need to be recognised to at least the same extent as we would expect to recognise the fears in our patients (clients).

One of the very common fears that is expressed as a reason for not accepting a client's request for help, is the fear of doing some sort of harm. Counsellors fear that they will leave the client in a worse state than that in which he was found. In counselling, as opposed to giving advice or information, we would argue that this is highly unlikely.

For any of us to assume that we have such power over another person, that enabling them to talk with us could do them actual harm, may be seen as quite arrogant. To allow another person to express his feelings, encouraging him to explore what these feelings really are and, by bringing them into the light, putting them into perspective and maybe working towards some kind of resolution is unlikely to do that person harm. Seen at its most negative, that is when resolution is nowhere near achieved, the very worst that can happen is for the client to remain in the position in which he started. He will not have been harmed.

To assume that the process described could be harmful to the client is to claim a Svengali-like power which very few, if any, of us possess. Equally, few, if any, of us are so powerless as to allow that sort of influence to be exerted upon us. For any of us to imagine that we have the sort of strength described is to deny the strength of the other person, to denigrate him.

We would suggest that the skilled counsellor can never actually damage the client. Pain may be experienced and the distress this engenders may be expressed. These feelings belong to the client. They have not been implanted by the counsellor. The counsellor has merely facilitated the acknowledgement of the fear and the pain. The authors hold most strongly that when the client is feeling warmth and acceptance of his feelings from the counsellor, he will not be harmed by them.

A more valid fear is that of not being able to rise to the occasion, a fear of our own inadequacy. This indeed is a fear we can all share to a greater or lesser degree. It is hardly surprising that, when we are entering into a counselling relationship, we ask ourselves if we have the skills and understanding required, or, if having been asked, we are not sure how to answer. We may well find ourselves looking at other areas of our lives in which we consider ourselves inadequate, and wondering not only whether we have the skills but if we have the right. We may so bemuse ourselves with questions of 'can' or 'should' that our introspection results in the client's being ignored or fobbed off in some way.

Counselling another person, who may have deep-seated inner conflicts, can be and often is a very humbling experience and one that often makes us acutely aware of our own inadequacies. This increased awareness can be very painful, so painful possibly, that we prefer not to look at it. Our pain may again prevent us from offering space to a client. We shall be looking at this concept more fully later.

The fear of not possessing sufficient skills is one that each of us has to face at one time or another. Skills can, however, be acquired and developed. They can be learned from courses, from reading and, most of all, they can be developed through supervised experience.

No one can fulfil the role of counsellor to their full potential unless they have a colleague with whom they can bounce their ideas, share their feelings and the stresses that are so often engendered, and gain the support and reassurance we all need. It is through this process, which the authors believe to be essential, that we can continually assess our own work, recognise our weaknesses and, equally important, recognise and acknowledge our strengths.

The value of planned supervision or consultation with a skilled colleague cannot be over-emphasised. It is far more than a case of two heads being better than one. There is the fulfilment of an over-riding need to clarify one's own thoughts by speaking them out loud to another person with the understanding of the process of counselling.

Perhaps one of the major areas of importance in supervision or in co-counselling is when a sense of failure is experienced. In the counselling context, success and failure are not easy terms to define. Feelings of failure are, however, very real, and as painful in this setting as in any other. The need to share them and to put these feelings into perspective is very strong and, we suggest, must be fulfilled if effective work is to be done.

Failure is not, of course, confined solely to the subjective impressions of the counsellor. There will be times when we do, in fact, fail. There will be times when we can be of no use at all to our client. This is not easy to accept, but for any of us to imagine that we have the solution to all the emotional ills of the world is, of course, unrealistic.

There is the possibility with every new client that, for a variety of reasons, we have nothing to offer.

It may be that, because of a clash of personalities, another counsellor may have more to offer. A counsellor may find a client repels her, or that the client's way of life is totally unacceptable to her. This is a comparatively rare occurrence, but needs to be acknowledged. Should a counsellor feel unable to empathise with a client for this sort of reason, it is realistic to suggest to the client that the counsellor feels unable to help but to suggest an alternative source — to give information as to where help could be sought.

It may be that the personality of the person seeking help is such that no counselling help is likely to be effective. Obviously the decision that a client is not likely to be helped is a difficult one to make and is not arrived at without a great deal of thought, even heart searching. The decision is one that supervision will help to make clear. The need for such a decision is sometimes not apparent until counselling has commenced or even for a considerable time after this. It is, however, a sad fact that there are personalities so damaged, through whatever cause, that they are beyond the range of the help of any counselling service. We need to accept this, and to recognise that the responsibility for the client's condition lies not within ourselves, but in the perhaps many years of emotional deprivation to which he has been subjected.

It may also be beyond our scope to enable the client to arrive at a solution for the difficulties in which he finds himself. There may be no solution. It may be that resolution will lie in the recognition of this, and an acceptance that there is going to be no change in the circumstances. The change that occurs must be in the client's attitude towards the situation.

The two aspects described, when the client is too damaged to come within the scope of counselling or when the problems of circumstances are intractable, are likely to be depressing to encounter. They may lead to feelings of being overwhelmed. It is often tempting in this situation to opt out of the counselling role and to begin to offer advice, telling the client what to do rather than allowing him the dignity of arriving at his own decisions. This is to court rejection.

People will, as a rule, do what they basically want to do, regardless of any advice anyone chooses to give them. Telling other people how to run their lives is a futile occupation, although apparently a popular one. If we, as counsellors, indulge ourselves in this way we must not be surprised if the person we are purporting to help rejects what we have to say.

If, moreover, we put the client into this position he is unlikely to bring us his feelings in the future. What seems to be an easy and acceptable way out of a dilemma in fact inhibits future contact of any real depth or value.

By telling people what to do, we block them from telling us what they want to do. Indeed, we block them from being able to be clear themselves about what they want to do. A marriage partner contemplating ending that partnership is going to be guided by his feelings. He may be confused about what those feelings actually are and may indeed be in need of help in clarifying those feelings and thoughts. The most effective way of preventing that process of clarification is for someone to tell that person what he 'ought to' do. 'Oughtism' is paralysing. 'Oughtism' prevents the client on whom it is imposed from moving on from where he is. It paralyses his ability to ask for help.

There are many ways in which we, as counsellors, can opt out of a counselling relationship if we choose to, at either a conscious or an unconscious level. Perhaps the greatest need is for us to be aware of what we are doing and why we are doing it.

We can choose, when we are asked for help, whether or not to respond.

We may dare to respond.

2.

NON-DIRECTIVE CLIENT-CENTRED COUNSELLING

The mode of counselling where the client is 'in charge' and the counsellor's role is seen as enabling the client, in various ways, to recognise and identify his own problems and find the solution or resolution for himself, has been described by Carl Rogers (1974). Rogers sees certain conditions as necessary for successful counselling which are summarised as follows.

Empathy. The counsellor, without prejudgements or assumptions, allows herself to be open to perceive the world as the client perceives it. She conveys this understanding to the client, mainly by reflection.

It is vital to realise that the world is to be perceived as the client perceives it. The medical profession has, at last, based the treatment of pain on the assumption that pain is what the patient feels. Not the pain he ought to feel, should feel, others have felt, but the pain he feels, is treated. Similarly, the problems a patient suffers are the problems of his world as he perceives it. When the counsellor shares that world, openly and without preconceptions, moral judgements or her own assumptions, only then can the counsellor begin to understand and communicate that understanding to her client. Only then can the client trust the counsellor enough to dare examine the areas of his experience he may feel are too shameful or painful to disclose.

Congruence. The counsellor recognises her own feelings and shares these with the client when this is appropriate.

Often a counsellor will become aware of her own feelings of anger, irritation, boredom, grief, when working with a client. It is all too easy to attribute these feelings to what the client is saying and to feel that the client is annoying or boring or over-dramatising. It is essential that the counsellor is able to recognise her own areas of unresolved feelings and to identify when the client, in relating his experiences, is impinging on the counsellor's experiences. He may come uncomfortably close to areas in which the counsellor has difficulties in her own life.

In a counselling relationship, both counsellor and client are open to the feelings of the other. A client who hears a counsellor say she is sympathetic and accepting when she is actually experiencing irritation and frustration, will sense this double message he is receiving and feel uneasy and insecure. It is therefore often appropriate for a counsellor experiencing strong emotion to share these feelings with the client. If, as suggested, the counsellor is aware of the reasons for her feelings, these reasons may be shared as well.

Such sharing helps in more than one way. The client is receiving clear messages from the counsellor. He gains confidence from the counsellor's openness. He may gain insight into his own reactions. He feels more acceptable himself and feels that the counsellor's admission of negative feelings gives him permission to acknowledge such feelings.

Non-possessive warmth. The counsellor communicates a concern for the whole person of the client, a concern that is not affected by any preconceived ideas or by any plans or decisions the counsellor may have been tempted to make for the client.

Real empathy almost invariably results in an involvement with the client's viewpoint and a real sympathy with his difficulties. If the counsellor is aware of her own preconceived ideas and judgements and consciously suspends these in her empathetic relationship with her client then a genuine warmth can ensue.

It is important that this warmth is communicated to the client. It is equally important that there should be no element of possessiveness in this warmth. Feeling possessive about the client may trap the counsellor into an attempt to guide the client into what the counsellor sees as the right way to act. The counsellor needs to remind herself that the only relevant and helpful recognition and resolution are what the client discovers for himself and relates to his world as he sees it.

Rogers describes a series of phases in the counselling relationship:

(a)   Emotional release
(b)   Gradual exploration of attitudes
(c)   Growing conscious awareness of denied elements
(d)   A changed perception of self in an altered frame of reference
(e)   A changed concept of self
(f)   A new course of consciously controlled action better adapted to the underlying reality
(g)   A resulting improvement in social and interpersonal relationships.

Consideration of this analysis will make clear how far the idea of non-directive, client-centred counselling is from giving good advice. It would seem to demand far more of the client than a submissive following of advice. It seems to demand far more of the counsellor than an accumulation of information and 'common sense' to be passed on judiciously.

The analysis implies, rather, a working relationship in which the dignity and self-respect of her client are fully acknowledged. It is a partnership in which the skills and informed intuition of the counsellor are utilised to enable the client to explore himself, a relationship of two people exercising mutual respect and warmth, in which hard work takes place.

Of all the skills Rogers describes as essential to achieve this counselling relationship, perhaps that of accepting warmth, a warmth without judgement or assumption, is the most difficult to understand. It is something most of us are not too familiar with. Much of the warmth we receive is conditional, or we impose our own conditions on its acceptance.

To experience a genuine warmth and regard which is based on recognition and acceptance of our whole selves, without overt or covert demands, is rare.

To accept such warmth without distrust or fear is indeed difficult. To feel worthy of such regard needs an acceptance of ourselves such as few of us fully achieve. To offer it requires the same. We must feel that such an offer is valuable and will not be rejected.

For practical purposes, when there is empathy and when the counsellor has accepted her own self-worth, warmth towards the client can be experienced without difficulty. Once it is accepted that judgements related to the counsellor's experiences are not relevant to the client, it is possible to be open to the client's world. Once having 'walked in another man's moccasins', in the words of the Sioux proverb, the counsellor will experience the flow of warmth towards the client that is one of the rewards of counselling.

The awareness of self and the valuing of that self is referred to in Chapter 5 and some exercises or 'games' are described.

These are important.

Counselling involves 'putting your whole self in', and the emphasis is on the word 'whole'. Wholeness of self is something that is only achieved by practising an awareness of our own motives, reactions and assumptions. It is necessary to recognise these, to accept them and, if we want to change, to do so in a positive way.

When we speak of the wholeness of self it is meant in most senses of the term. With a growing acceptance of self-worth, there can come an increasing awareness of one's own skills. Moreover, the value of those skills can begin to be appreciated to a greater level.

There is a need, it seems, to recognise that many skills, which we may take for granted and which may seem to be mundane, can in fact be used in an appropriate counselling situation, even though they would not normally be accepted as counselling skills as such.

Making a cup of coffee, for example, may not be seen as a very skilful operation. For some people, however, making a cup of coffee and serving it to the counsellor is, because of disability, a very skilful act indeed. Because the counsellor knows something, not only of the nature of disability but also what is involved in making coffee, it might be possible to use that act in a positive manner in subsequent counselling sessions.

All of us, in the course of our daily lives, acquire skills of various types and in various ways. Any of these skills can, though not necessarily will, be used in some way, perhaps in some far distant counselling session. A counsellor in training recently spoke of a client with whom it seemed impossible for her to establish a rapport. The counsellor had, many years previously, trained in floristry. She used flower arranging as an analogy when speaking to her client of the difficulties they were experiencing in establishing a relationship. Because the counsellor knew what she was talking about, both in terms of floristry and counselling, the client was enabled to recognise the difficulties too, and to begin to 'rearrange her own flowers'.

Appreciation of self involves a recognition of one's own qualities, each of which will have its own intrinsic value. It is also true, though, that many attributes that we have, or acquire along the way, can in some circumstances be used in a very real sense in counselling. To be too proud to use them, or indeed too shy, is false. Salvador Minuchin (1977) has suggested that the 'only you I know is me'. The only real tool I have is myself. Not to use all of myself, then, means making a less than optimum performance.

Change or growth can take place but only if we feel that it would enhance our lives and relationships, or enable us to function more effectively. Conscious effort to change will not be effective if it is initiated by a feeling that one has failed to be an acceptable person.

The training for most of the paramedical professions involves the students experiencing the treatments they will be expected to administer. Similarly, the counsellor needs to experience an unconditional warmth towards herself before she is truly able to feel this for her client.

Confrontation. The aspect of client-centred counselling that can be described as creative listening (as opposed to a passive acceptance of all the client says) arises most directly from the skill of congruence. This is described as confrontation.

Without this, it can be all too easy for the client to gain comfort and reassurance from a warm, accepting counsellor without making any progress in resolving his difficulties. The client may recognise and identify his problems but come no nearer to finding solutions or resolution.

The counsellor who is touch with her own feelings will soon become aware of the client who is 'stuck'. The counsellor may feel bored or irritated. She will recognise that the client is repeating himself or demanding a particular reaction from her.

To point this out to the client, to confront him with what he is doing, can provide the impetus he needs to move on.

This can be done in a way that is not destructive to the client. The way confrontation is handled will depend to a great extent on the personalities of both client and counsellor and on the relationship between them. Possible confronting statements in a counselling session in which the counsellor has become aware that the client seems to be going over the same ground without any new insights, could be:

'That story really seems to worry you. I wonder why you are telling me about it again?'

'Yes, I remember you telling me about that. What do you want to do about these feelings? What can you do next?'

'You seem to be stuck. I wonder if there is something you are avoiding talking about?'

'You seem to be asking me for some different reaction to that story. I am wondering what you want from me?'

The client may indeed become angry if he is confronted. The counsellor is able to accept the anger and refer to it. This anger can be a very useful thing and, with the acceptance of the counsellor, may well lead to new insight. The client will then be enabled to move further on towards recognition or resolution.

Once the counsellor has accepted anger from the client and has remained warm and supportive despite the client's strong and 'unacceptable' feelings, the value of confrontation will be proved in the development of insight.

This will occur if the client is indeed ready and willing to become aware of his difficulties and to work towards resolution.

Should such a result not be apparent, it may be that the client is not ready or willing. In this case, the counsellor may need to decide if the counselling relationship is an appropriate one. Further confrontation may be necessary to clarify with the client what he is asking for. If this is sympathy or an unquestioning, unchallenging receptacle for his complaints then counselling is inappropriate and the counsellor needs to be clear what she is prepared to offer.

This clarification of the exact relationship between client and counsellor is the counselling contract. The making of this contract is discussed further in Chapter 7.

REFERENCES

Minuchin, S. (1977) *Families and Family Therapy*. Tavistock Publications, London.

Rogers, C. (1974) *On Becoming a Person* Constable, London.

3.

COUNSELLING BEN

The Prologue set the scene, the previous two chapters have outlined counselling principles and in this chapter we put them together to demonstrate the art of counselling.

The physical symptoms of multiple sclerosis (MS) can give rise to psychological difficulties that many of those involved with the MS sufferer find hard to allow themselves to recognise.

MS is a disease of uncertainty, its diagnosis, course, prognosis and management all falling into the realm of speculation. The sufferer is also uncertain of many aspects of his daily life, and an activity feasible one day may be impossible the next. Unexpected and often very sudden fatigue, not unlike that following influenza, may result in a humiliating fall or embarrassing social mishap. Bladder weakness, blurred vision or hand tremor can make even undemanding situations threatening to self-esteem. It is difficult to plan even a day or two ahead with any real certainty, or so it seems to the victim in the early or more acute states.

Uncertainty, and the fears that it engenders, can eventually be integrated into an acceptable quality of life and strategies can be evolved to cope with physical symptoms, but time and often skilled help are needed.

Alexander and Penelope Burnfield, who are both doctors and counsellors with personal experience of MS, have found in research (1978) that 'some doctors feel unprepared emotionally to deal either with the patient's problems or their own feelings of inadequacy'. We have found that medical and paramedical students are still taught that euphoria is a symptom of MS, whereas depression is much more common. It would seem that denial on the part of the professionals, so frequently a reaction to feelings of inadequacy, is operating here. In our experience, and that of other experienced counsellors, this euphoria is spurious, being usually a conditioned response to those involved in their care. These carers, overtly or covertly, consciously or unconsciously, are demanding exactly that response.

For example, patients in hospital, their powers of decision and choice denied them, unquestioning conformity apparently demanded of them by necessity, usually give up their adult status voluntarily. Only then are the demands of dependence and submission to painful or humiliating procedures, even the ultimate surrender of consciousness in anaesthesia, made bearable. In this new, child-like state the patient is very sensitive to the demands made on him. Many of us find that it is too painful to empathise with the fear, the confusion and the depression of many patients, so we deny it. By that denial, we demand that the patient wastes no time in coming to terms with his 'bereavement'. Even when we are unable to imagine such a feat, we impose on the patient an unnatural acceptance, or euphoria. Thus, we protect and comfort ourselves. The patient, with unacknowledged and unrecognised feelings, experiences more inadequacy, more rejection, increased depression, and begins to doubt his own reality.

We use the word 'bereavement', which may seem inappropriate, as a valid synonym for many of the effects of debility or illness. Bereavement implies loss, and loss is indeed experienced. Loss of function, loss of acceptable body image, loss of self-esteem and identity, loss of libido, impotence in some cases, loss of skills, job, even partner or lover, and a real or imagined loss of social status can all result from, for example, MS. Nor does this loss have to be of things actually experienced. The congenitally disabled feel bereaved of the opportunity to experience whatever their disability denies them and their loss is just as real. As in all bereavement, denial, anger, grief, fear, guilt, depression, may all need to be recognised and worked through before acceptance and/or resolution can begin to be truly achieved. The work of grieving needs to be completed (see Chapter Ten).

The Burnfields further state that 'the psychological problems of MS often cause more suffering than the physical effects.' Ben, the subject of the Prologue, is demonstrably receiving excellent care with regards to his physical needs and practical difficulties. Various reasons indicate that his emotional needs are being denied. Ben feels that there is no one to accept his negative feelings, so he assumes such feelings are unacceptable. He is ashamed of himself, ashamed of being himself and finds himself unacceptable. He tries, then, to make his shameful, unacceptable self conform to what he perceives as the standards of acceptability of the people on whom he now seems to be dependent.

For the moment, this role, the role of the well-adjusted man who can cope with everything that a cruel fate has thrown at him, grateful for his wonderful wife, grateful for the care he receives, grateful that he is not as badly off as some others, fighting down the unworthy thoughts, is an effective role. The stress of maintaining it is almost intolerable, however, and any additional strain may destroy it.

Why, then, is this role apparently being demanded of Ben? If any of us become disabled as a result of disease or trauma, it is far too easy for most of the rest to see only physical change. Indeed, it can be positively inviting. If we look simply at the physical change, and reassure ourselves by doing all we can to alleviate the physical effects, we are not forced to look any further.

If we are brave enough, we may even search a little deeper and acknowledge the known psychological effects of that particular condition. It is then not difficult to believe that all that can be done is being done, and to believe that the patient is receiving the best of all possible treatments. It is then, perhaps, that we are likely to become a little complacent, that we can begin to congratulate ourselves. We assuage any uneasy feelings by the assurance that we are doing a good job in a difficult situation.

If those of us who are concerned with disability lull ourselves into this state, it is hardly likely that we are going to recognise the signs that may tell us something of the distress the patient is suffering.

Our failure to make this recognition is compounded by the patient himself. The result may be a game at which we can all become expert, a game in which we jolly one another along, and the patient represses many of the feelings he is experiencing but which the world does not let him express.

One aspect of acquired disability can be the very great change in roles which society expects and which the patient feels he has to endure. To return to Ben, the change in role that he has been forced to accept, from being a busy newspaper reporter, travelling the world, to being virtually housebound, is obvious. The shrinkage of his world is quite plain to see. The distress and disappointment that this change has caused are also obvious. If we make ourselves a little more aware, however, there are several other role changes which are not perhaps so immediately apparent.

Ben's previous roles have been those of husband, father and breadwinner, in which he led an exciting and fulfilling life. Each of these roles has been changed by his illness. In each of these changes Ben has been diminished.

He is no longer the husband on whom his wife depends for support. The reversal of their roles has in fact occurred. It is now Ben who checks the time the children should be home from school. Ben copes as best he can with the household chores and tries to gain satisfaction from a pile of ironing. It is Ben who is at home to answer the front door, Ben who waits for his wife to come home from work. Of course (it would seem) Ben must feel pleased and excited that his wife, in contrast to himself, has such a good job. To feel anything else would be ungrateful — and no disabled person is allowed ingratitude. Ben must never acknowledge, even to himself, his feelings of jealousy, resentment, grief, about the stimulation and enjoyment his wife receives from her work. Neither must he compare her feelings with his own limited achievements of the day.

When Jean took a full-time job Ben was relieved of financial worries. Before he became disabled such money troubles, as there were, were Ben's. He may not have enjoyed worrying about the mortgage, but freedom from worry was perhaps something he could give to Jean. Now that facet of his life, along with so many others, had been taken from him. Not only were they taken, but were given to the very person who had previously been dependent on him.

It becomes more complex than this. There is more than this simple reversal of dependency. The fact of being dependent on his wife for money would perhaps be difficult for Ben to accept, but he is, in addition, expected to feel pleased and excited about it. To be anything else would appear as ungrateful. The expectations of his wife, his family and his friends are likely to be that Ben should be happy that Jean is able to support him and the children in this way. Ben is given no option but to agree that he is lucky. It may be that his deeper, unacknowledged feelings are that he has very little to be happy about, that his luck ran out along with his physical fitness.

Ben is also expected to count himself lucky in respect of selling his car, for such a good price, to the man who took the job Ben was no longer able to perform. Ben must count himself lucky to sell the car he treasured, that had been his, his envied possession. Now there is just the family car, referred to by Ben as 'the car' and eventually as 'Jean's car'.

A man's car is often associated with his personality. When that car is coveted it is often symbolic of his status and masculinity. In Ben's case, it had to go — along with his status and at least some of his masculinity. The symbolism must not be considered insignificant. Compounding this is Jean's capable nature. She knows how to look after a car. He cannot even tell Jean what needs to be done, she already knows. Spared worry about the car as well, Ben is further diminished.

Jean, acting from the best of motives, is doing everything she can to relieve Ben of worries. The result is that Ben has no more responsibility than performing household chores, which he knows Jean could perform more effectively in every way.

Every responsibility of which Ben is relieved diminishes him. He is quite aware of his wife's kindly motivation and, aware that it is for the best and perhaps inevitable, is forced to be pleased at his good fortune in having such a wife. He is then in the paradoxical situation of having to be happy about being unable to fulfil what he sees as his real function.

Jean has taken over Ben's role almost completely and she has done so without fuss. How can Ben allow himself to fuss if Jean does not? This quiet, tactful, efficient taking over has denied Ben the very basic need to talk about his feelings.

The enormity of not 'talking about it' is perhaps highlighted by Ben's recognition that Jean could manage at least as well if he was dead. Implicitly, Ben is acknowledging that he is a burden. Explicitly, he recognises Jean's frustration at his slowness and awkwardness. He is not given the opportunity to explore these feelings and has to resort to a spurious feeling of satisfaction at having carried out what he regards as a menial household task — the ironing.

Seen in this light, Ben's attempts to assume the housewife's role become pathetic. It is not a role he chose for himself and, however hard he tries to convince himself that there is no stigma attached to such a role, for Ben there is a stigma. For him, it is demeaning and diminishing and, moreover, he cannot even do it well. Despite the great welter of emotion this knowledge engenders, Ben still feels it is necessary to assure himself that 'there didn't even seem to be any need to talk about it'.

The reality is, of course, that Ben has never been allowed to talk about it. No one has ever given him the necessary permission. For Ben to express his feelings without such permission — that is, without someone creating an atmosphere in which he is allowed to talk — would seem to Ben to be indulging in self-pity. There may be other negative feelings involved for Ben in talking about his own feelings, but self-pity is prominent as one which Ben is not allowed. He has, along with so many of us, been well conditioned over many years into believing that feeling sorry for oneself is shameful. The very term 'self-pity' is usually used in a derogatory sense, while it is acceptable or admirable to feel sorry for someone else.

Perhaps the concept of self-pity as a despicable character trait is one we could all query. There are, for example, many people worse off than Ben, for whom he should feel sorry. He meets some of them during his physiotherapy sessions. Is pointing this out to Ben really expected to make him feel better? Is it somehow more realistic, more acceptable for Ben to feel sorrow at their fate but to ignore his own?

Is not, perhaps, the notion of Ben counting his blessings rather an unconscious device to stop him from complaining and thus making the rest of us feel bad too? Optimism is so much more acceptable to most of us, often to the extent that we do not allow any natural fears and depression to be acknowledged and worked through so that it can be put in its proper perspective.

Ben leaves his physiotherapy class feeling let down and miserable. He feels put to shame by the children he sees there, who perhaps also remind him of demands made on him as a child to suppress grief and anger and 'behave like a big boy'.

Ben does not feel genuinely able to share the atmosphere of apparent optimism. There seem to have been assumptions from staff and patients that Ben would conform, that he would accept the role of 'good patient' and live up to the demands of the label he has not chosen.

What does this role of being a 'good patient' demand? Apparently, that Ben should not only accept the severe limitations of his disease but accept them cheerfully and with a sense of optimism. For Ben to step outside these expectations would be to earn another label, one most feared by the patient, that of being 'difficult'. Few patients want to risk that, not only because they want to be seen as nice and therefore acceptable, but because of an underlying, unconscious fear that to be seen as difficult and ungrateful might endanger that which is needed for survival.

Surviving is almost all that is left for Ben in his present situation, all that is left for him as an individual. He may be able to experience some vicarious fulfilment through other people, notably his children. It can be argued, of course, that all parents wish to some extent to live through their children, but for Ben, yet again, there is no choice. Yet again, his traditional role has been substituted by another, ill-defined expectation. From being the important member of the family, returning from trips abroad with exciting gifts and interesting stories, he is relegated to the part of housewife with nothing to relate but the spilling of a bowl of sugar, no gift to offer but the clean laundry. It is Jean and the children who inhabit the real, exciting world and it is Jean and the children from whom Ben must now gain his experiences.

Having a new body image to accept, a change that is forced on his attention with his every activity, Ben cannot help but be aware that his children are conscious of his altered state as well. They have to explain to themselves and to their friends the fact of a father who is different. They will possibly hear derogatory remarks about a father who does not go to work, who lurches along on two sticks. They have to face the loss of an active, energetic, exciting parent. They too are bereaved, and Ben's awareness of this enhances his own grief, resentment and guilt. He feels he has nothing to give them, no future to offer them, no way of expressing his love and concern for them in any practical or material way. He cannot give his time and skill to Tim in choosing to kick a football around or express his attention to and admiration of Sue in taking her to dancing class and watching her lesson.

Ben is expressing a bewildering turmoil of emotions and there seems to be no one who recognises and accepts that he may not be a fortunate, well-adapted man with a supportive and understanding family, coping admirably with a stable condition of MS. Anyone offering the opportunity and permission for Ben to talk about his feelings might see a very different picture. There are many clues in Ben's thoughts as we have recorded them and there would equally be indications in his spoken communication with those he talks to.

The words we use to express our thoughts, opinions and feelings may be consciously chosen to convey the most accurate impression to a listener. Subconsciously we frequently choose words or phrases that betray our deeper feelings. The 'Freudian slip', for example, when an apparently inadvertent mistake can provide a very accurate guide to the speaker's feelings, illustrates how apposite these choices can be. A delightful written example of such a slip was received by one of the authors when the writer stated that, when being with a particular group of people, he had not felt any 'aggrrression'.

The apparently accidental (and certainly unrecognised by the writer) inclusion of extra letters so that the word included the threatening 'grrr' were far more indicative to his real feelings than his confident assertion. When he was challenged about this he was able to talk about how irritating he had, in fact, found one member of the group, and how angry that no one had supported him in a disagreement with her.

Ben's choice of metaphor, had his thoughts been spoken instead of being presented as uncommunicated musings, would give us some insight into his deeper feelings. His description of his wife Jean as someone who 'took everything in her stride' highlights his own inability to walk without great difficulty. His change of pronoun when describing Jean's job, when his assertion that '*they* were still feeling excited' changes in emphasis to '*she* enjoyed it so much' is a clue to Ben's very mixed feelings about Jean becoming the wage-earner of the family.

Ben refers to 'playing the role' of housewife. Now much of his life is playing a role or acting a part.

The word 'cope' — first used by Ben in his thoughts about the housework — is one frequently encountered in connection with disabled people and their families. Ben, for example, wonders about the family of the quadriplegic young man coping with the physical demands involved. Chambers 20th Century Dictionary defines 'cope' as 'to contend — to deal (with) successfully'. This seems a tight-lipped, joyless enduring of the apparently inevitable.

Had Ben used such terms when talking with a counsellor he could have been enabled to recognise, and then begin to accept and work towards resolving, the feelings behind such a choice of language.

Reflecting, that is saying back to the client the words he has used or what the counsellor perceives as what he is saying, can often result in such recognition. For example (B = Ben, C = Counsellor):

B. I thought for a moment that the tremor was worse, but it was only my overactive imagination again.

C. You feel your imagination is overactive?

B. It must be the only part of me that is — overactive, I mean.

C. You don't feel that the rest of you is overactive?

B. You have to be joking! How could anyone describe me as even active? I can't even carry my own coffee across the room . . .

It can be observed that Ben had already begun to express his real feelings. This example is not over-simplified, and what may read as a slightly artificial comment by the counsellor is not apparent as such in practice.

Ben had evolved, probably half-consciously, a strategy by which he could approach his social worker. Ben identified to a considerable extent with the young man with quadriplegia. In some ways, that young man represented Ben's fears about his own future, should Ben regress to a stage of physical dependence. If the social worker had had time for the discussion Ben had hoped for, her response might have enabled him to express his own fears.

The strategy of asking for advice or information concerning a third person is a common approach, minimising the risk of rejection or disapproval, and is familiar to many counsellors. It may vary from the adolescent's 'I've got this friend who's got this problem', to Ben's very real concern for a fellow patient. It is a way of assessing the likely response to a more direct disclosure.

Once such an approach is recognised by the counsellor, it can be acknowledged and the counsellor can, in effect, give permission for the client to share his feelings.

In the following imagined dialogue, the social worker uses reflection. Another skill demonstrated is congruence, the sharing of the counsellor's own feelings and reactions with the client (when appropriate) (B = Ben, S = Social Worker):

B. I was wondering, I wanted to ask you — you know John, the young guy at the hospital, the one who had the bike smash?

S. I'm not sure if I do know him — tell me about him.

B. Well, he's ended up almost completely paralysed; he always will be.

S. Yes, I do know John.

B. I was wondering, well, I mean, what happens to him when he leaves the hospital?

S. You are worried about where he will go?

B. Well, yes. I mean no one could expect his family to cope.

S. You feel that a family can't be expected to cope with all the work entailed in looking after a paralysed man?

B. Right. So where will he go?

S. You know that there are, of course, several possibilities for helping the family to manage. For instance, support, adaptations, even special housing. But if that isn't the answer, well, it's really difficult, having to face that decision. It's one of the things I find hardest. There are, of course, several different kinds of residential care available.

B. Residential care? Institutions, you mean?

S. You sound angry — bitter.

B. Well, why not? How would feel if you were suddenly unable to do anything for yourself and they got rid of you into an institution?

S. I don't know. I really can't imagine. It sounds as if you have, imagined it I mean.

Ben can now choose — and the choice is his — whether to retreat to the safer ground of his original opening gambit or to disclose his own fears.

The acceptance and recognition are, of course, necessary before Ben can continue. Recognition is the first step on the part of the counsellor. However, there are many responses other than that illustrated, many responses that do not acknowledge the request, and familiar rebuffs for the person seeking help.

B. I was wanting to ask you, what is going to happen to John when he leaves hospital?

S. Well, he will have been physically assessed by the physio and the speech therapist, the OT [occupational therapist] will give a full report on her investigations and he may attend a course at a rehabilitation centre. There will be a full case conference, the family being consulted, and an appropriate referral will be made. We have a very good record of placements at this hospital.

To give information is easy to justify, and in this case the social worker no doubt feels she has answered Ben's question more than adequately. Her failure — for whatever reason — to recognise what Ben really wants to know, effectively blocks Ben from continuing the dialogue.

B. Do you know what will happen to John when he leaves the hospital?

S. I wouldn't worry about that if I were you. I should leave problems like that to all the people who are qualified to deal with them. If you take my advice you'll concentrate on your own plans. In my experience, clients can get very depressed worrying about things they really don't know much about. Let's discuss that swimming group I mentioned to you last week. You need a challenge, something to keep you busy.

Giving advice is another response that reassures the giver but seldom satisfies the one asking. It is too easy to feel that the 'onlooker sees more of the game', easy to feel that a detached but concerned observer can see the right, the obvious way for a client to behave. It seems to the giver that good advice based on that view will be useful.

It is important to recognise that there is no absolute right or wrong way to respond to any situation. A choice of action that might be appropriate for one person in his perception of his circumstances, may be inappropriate or even disastrous for another. It is each person's perception of his life, not how it appears to anyone else, that is significant.

The phrase 'if I were you' is meaningless in this context. 'I' can never be 'you', and my perception of the world can never be yours. I can only share such views of your world as you are willing and able to share with me.

B. What will happen to John?

S. Oh, he's doing really well, he'll be fine, don't you worry. There are lots of people looking after John; he'll be fine.

Facile and meaningless reassurance is an insult to the recipient and demonstrates an avoidance on the part of its giver. It is frequently a denial of the possibility of there being any problem, a kind of sympathetic magic, working on the assumption that a fact denied may be ignored. Such a denial — 'John will be fine' — when it is very obvious that John has horrifying problems, is very disturbing to someone such as Ben. He, fully aware of John's serious difficulties, will now feel that his own less obvious fears are dismissed.

B. Where will John go when he leaves?

S. Well, you know I can't discuss another patient with you. It would not be fair on him and would be most unprofessional on my part. The DRO [disablement resettlement officer] and the patient's own social worker are the people basically concerned with that problem. If you have any valid reason for wanting to know, they would be the correct people to consult.

The social worker's response is, of course, quite correct. Referral to the appropriate expert — defining clearly her own area of professional responsibility — is a correct and safe response. Such a response, however, is all too frequently a 'cop-out'. The term cop-out is used to describe a rationalised response that absolves the speaker from the need to perceive and respond to the client's real need.

Of course there are occasions when information, reassurances and, rarely, advice are all appropriate. In all circumstances the need for counselling should be recognised. The authors have sometimes used a simplistic illustration of this:

A patient appeals to a member of the hospital staff, saying, 'The left wheel of my chair is falling off'. He meets with a variety of responses:

'The wheelchair mechanic is in Room 234.' (Information).

'If I were you, I'd get that fixed. In my experience, you will be in trouble if that wheel falls off.' (Advice).

'Now don't you worry, everything will be alright.' (Facile and meaningless reassurance).

'I'm not qualified to repair wheelchairs; you should see the mechanic.' (Referral to an expert).

'You sound upset. How do you feel about the risk of being left with only three wheels?' (The counselling approach).

Although the last response may sound unhelpful regarding the original complaint and clearly the loose wheel must be attended to, it may be that the loss of the wheel arouses painful reminders in the patient's consciousness of his own physical dependence and vulnerability. These feelings need exploring and resolving.

The response of the social worker in the original scenario, in which she acknowledges Ben's feelings and enables him to begin to recognise and explore them, assumes some skills in counselling in the social worker. The authors have also suggested that a client will ask someone he feels he can trust to accept his confidences. This person may well not be a trained counsellor, an expert. If you recognise that such an approach is being made to you, should you respond?

If someone trusts that you can help, then you are probably the right one to help. The choice whether or not to respond is yours. Should you feel unable to make that response, that choice will be right for you in your perception of the demands that are being made on you and of your ability to respond.

However, some of the fears that may prevent a counsellor, one who is asked, from responding, may be recognised by that counsellor. The recognition of these fears may result in an altered perception of the situation and a different response.

REFERENCE

Burnfield, A. and Burnfield, P. (1978) Common psychological problems in multiple sclerosis. *B.M.J.* I, 1193–1194.

4.

ROLE-PLAY

It is perhaps poor practice to begin a definition by explaining what a term does *not* mean, but we have found such a widespread range of misunderstanding of role-play that initially two statements seem useful:

Role-play is not acting.

Role-play is not pretending.

We have described the skill of empathy, and role-play is, in many ways, a development of this.

When practising empathy, the counsellor is attempting to perceive the world as the client sees it, suspending the counsellor's own assumptions and judgements. In role-play, the player starts with some facts about the subject and then allows himself to experience the feelings that are aroused when he describes how these facts affect him. These feelings are not simulated, but real and deeply experienced by the player. The counsellor can enable the player to recognise feelings that can be very far from those the player may have imagined as relevant to the role.

The feelings of the person playing the role are, of course, his own. These may, at first sight, bear little relationship to the person whose experiences have been used as a starting point for the player and the counsellor. In practice, however, we have found role-play to be most valuable in a number of ways.

To widen the counsellor's experience

Working with people in distress inevitably seems to lead to an attempt to imagine what it must be like, for example, to have a progressive illness, to be bereaved, to have a drastically reduced life expectancy. The authors have found this feat of imagination an impossible one to achieve.

Using role-play, feeling the circumstances rather than intellectualising them, has brought us a little nearer to grasping 'how it feels'. It has widened our own knowledge of the sometimes unexpected and unimagined responses that distress may initiate.

To provide greater sensitivity in specific areas

In supervision, using the skills of a colleague in consultation over the counselling process, role-play can be of great assistance in understanding what may be happening for a client when there are difficulties. The counsellor plays her client and the supervisor acts as counsellor.

This process seems on occasion to enable the player to use insights and observed intuition about the client that she may not have felt able to risk sharing with him. Indeed, she may be unaware of what she has observed and perceived.

In role-play the counsellor can test the validity of such insight, which will often help the counselling directly.

We have sometimes told clients that we have had certain feelings when role-playing their experiences. When the client recognises these feelings as duplicating his own, the sense of affirmation he feels has often meant a leap forward in the counselling process. When he is able to recognise the feelings but explain where they differ from his own, a clarification of his feelings often results.

To experience painful emotions in a 'safe' place

Most of us find difficulty in expressing painful emotions at the time they are initiated. It may be too frightening. It may be inappropriate. We may feel unable to cope with what we imagine the consequences would be. We may feel guilty about such feelings (the authors both remember feelings of almost murderous rage at the continual screaming of a very young baby, and the accompanying guilt and fear that we should feel such anger at our own child).

In role-play, feelings of grief or anger that are entirely appropriate to the role are often experienced in great intensity and are expressed by the player.

It is safe to express such feelings in the role of another person. To feel and express rage or anguish, to allow previously forbidden emotions to be demonstrated, can be a valuable catharsis. Once such feelings have been released the player is often later able to talk about her own suppressed experiences.

DE-ROLING

Because role-play often releases strongly felt emotions, and because the player may be deeply into the role, it is vitally important that she has the time and help to come out of it and then clearly identify what belongs to the role and what belongs to her real life.

The counsellor working with the player has several techniques for assisting de-roling, the most simple (and that used in the role-play of Tim which follows) is to ask the player, when the role-play is finished, to identify herself by name, to give her address, details of her family and to describe her work.

Moving from the chair in which the player sat during her role-play, talking to the counsellor in her real person and perhaps having a cup of tea or coffee, also help.

A discussion usually follows role-play and the player may find herself using the first person singular in describing feelings engendered during the session. A second de-roling is then important at the end of the discussion.

In the previous chapter the authors examined Ben's feelings about his illness and suggested how he could be helped to recognise and express them through the skills of a counsellor. Many of Ben's difficulties inevitably centre around what he perceives as altered relationships with his wife, his son, his daughter and other people he meets.

It has been said that a disabled person means a disabled family, and in Ben's case this would apparently be the truth. In order to consider Ben as a whole person, we need to look at him in the context of the people with whom he most closely relates.

The feelings the authors have ascribed to Ben are those we, as counsellors, have identified as a result of our own direct contact with clients. We have decided to use a different technique in order to look at the way in which Ben's illness affects his wife and one of his children. This is the technique of role-play.

The transcripts which follow are edited tape recordings. The author respectively played the roles of Jean, Ben's wife, and Tim, Ben's elder child.

The counsellor is a psychotherapist who works largely in the transactional analysis mode (see Chapter 5). The authors discussed the situation of Ben and his family at great length during the writing of this book. The counsellor knew only that Ben had multiple sclerosis and that he had a wife, Jean, and two children, a boy and girl.

The background to the role-play was that Jean asked for help with nine-year-old Tim, who seemed to be disturbed.

Both role-plays took 30 minutes, and each was observed by the author not role-playing. Both authors and the counsellor discussed each role-play immediately afterwards. These discussions were also tape recorded.

TRANSCRIPT OF INTERVIEW WITH TIM

(C = Counsellor, T = Tim)
C. What did you want to talk about, Tim?
T. I don't want to talk about anything. I came because my Mum told me to.
C. What did she tell you . . . did she tell you why she wanted you to come?
T. Well, she seemed to think I ought to talk about Dad.
C. Do you want to talk about Dad?
T. Nothing to say. There's just my Dad. He's — um — he can't do things like he used to, and that's all there is to it.
C. What kind of things used he to do?
T. He did all sorts of things. He used to go abroad a lot, bring us back presents and things like that. Can't do anything now.
C. Did you enjoy the presents?
T. Yes, of course I did. But it was good when Dad came home. It was always good when Dad came home.
C. What was good about it?

T.   Well, he was there. Mum's OK; I don't mean that, but it was special when Dad was there. There was . . . you know, you always had time to talk and laugh and play around and do things. It wasn't just silly things, it was just . . . just different when he was there.

C.   So you were probably used to him going away a lot?

T.   Oh yes. But he always came back.

C.   It sounds like he gave you an awful lot of attention.

T.   Well, he was young, yes, he was there. It was good, it was fun. He would laugh, joke, tell us things that had happened when he'd been away.

C.   And now?

T.   Now he doesn't go anywhere, except to hospital.

C.   So he's home a lot? What do you think about that?

T.   Well he can't help it, can he? He's not well.

C.   Do you know what's the matter with him?

T.   It's called MS.

C.   Do you know what that's about?

T.   Well, no. They can't cure it, they can't make it better. It's not fair.

C.   What's not fair about it?

T.   Well, why should it be my Dad? He was good. He played. He was fun — funny. Now he can't be. Anyway, I don't want to talk about it.

C.   Does it hurt? That he can't be fun any more?

T.   Of course it hurts. That's a silly question.

C.   Doesn't it feel like all the good times are gone?

T.   Well, they are. All the — yes, they are.

C.   That must be sad-making for you, Tim.

T.   Of course it is. Nobody cares much. Nobody at — nobody at school cares or understands, if they care they don't understand; they don't know what it's like. Mum cares, I don't mean that. But she's too busy. She's always busy.

C.   Well, what is she too busy to do with you?

T.   Anything. The house is clean and Dad does a lot about that. She sees that we have our dinners and all that sort of thing. She doesn't have any time; she goes to work now, she's got to. Somebody's got to. Dad can't. He would if he could.

C.   What used you to do with your Mum before she started working?

T.   Not much, I suppose, really. Look, we did things like — oh, I don't know, things everybody does, like watch the telly, pick up a newspaper, listen to the radio. If she was there when I got home from school, she'd say 'How d'you get on?' Didn't often tell her, but, you know, she'd always ask. Now she's . . now she's too busy to ask. She has to rush straight in and do whatever it is that has to be done.

C.   It seems like there's no time for you any more.

T.   Oh, Mum doesn't have the time.

C.   Have you been able to talk with her, Tim?

T.   What chance is there to talk? She comes in, she's got dinner to cook or serve up or something. All she wants to talk about is her new job, and how well she's getting on at it, what all the people said at work. And all Dad wants to talk about is what they said at the hospital. And yet, mustn't ask too many questions about what they said at the hospital, because that upsets Dad.

C. So you've got to be careful with Dad, and Mum's too busy to talk.

T. Well, she can't help it. She's got reasons, if she's got to go to work.

C. It also sounds like the job is important to her. It brings her a lot of satisfaction.

T. I know that. She's always talking about it.

C. Sometimes, Tim, what has happened in families, is that the parents get too big. Big parents get so involved with what they're doing that they forget about the kids sometimes. They forget to ask what's going on with — with you and your sister, for example.

T. Well, Mum's got Dad to worry about.

C. So are you saying you don't want her to worry about you?

T. Well, there's nothing to worry about apart from that.

C. You really feel that, Tim?

T. Yes.

C. You're angry and you're hurt about this going on?

T. Well, I'm alright. I'm doing all right at school. Well, not too bad.

C. So how are things at school?

T. Well, not too bad. I get on . . . well . . . yes. All right, really.

C. Do you get on with the other kids at school?

T. Some of them.

C. What about the teachers?

T. Well, teachers . . . are teachers, aren't they? They're just — just there to teach you; they don't want to know about anything else.

C. So everywhere you go, Tim, there's nobody to talk with. You have to be careful with Dad, teachers do their business and that's it. You get on with some of the kids, but you said earlier that they don't understand really.

T. You can't tell them about your Dad who can't do anything, can you?

C. Are you embarrassed about your Dad?

T. Well, other kids talk about all going and playing football with their Dad or something like that. What can I say? I helped him wipe up, or do the dishes? Big deal, isn't it?

C. So there aren't situations you can talk about any more, and be proud about?

T. Well I haven't *got* 'em, have I? That's that. I've got to put up with it.

C. I agree with you that it's probably the way you're going to have to live, and that you're going to have to put up with a lot of things. There have been major changes in your family.

T. I know. And they're getting worse.

C. But that doesn't mean you don't have the right to talk.

T. What good's that going to do? It's not going to make Dad better.

C. Has your Dad ever been able to talk to you about his feelings?

T. It wouldn't do any good, would it? Like, he would do if it would help, but it wouldn't. It wouldn't make any difference, it couldn't alter things. It would only make him feel worse, so . . .

C. That I'm not sure about. I agree it wouldn't alter things, but usually people feel better after they've talked about their hurts and their sadnesses . . . and feeling powerless, feeling they can't do things any longer.

T. But he can't do things any longer, that's what it's all about.

C. And usually people have feelings about that. About not being . . .

T. [interrupts] But I can't alter it, can I?

C. No, you don't have that kind of power. Nor that kind of magic.

T. So, what . . . what good is it going to do? I ask Dad how he feels, and he says, 'OK' or 'I'm not too bad', or 'About the same as usual' or something like that.

C. So he seems strong, just like you.

T. You've got to be, haven't you?

C. It's really hard, you being so hard on yourself, Tim. You so strong and feeling so much about the situation.

T. You've got to be strong. No point going around crying about it all the time, is there? I don't cry, anyway.

C. You look like you're starting to.

T. I'm not . . . I don't need to cry.

C. Sounds like your Dad needs to cry.

T. Ah, but he wouldn't. It's all right for Sue, she's a girl.

C. Does she cry?

T. Sometimes.

C. And who does she cry to?

T. I don't know.

C. Does she ever cry to you?

T. Yes, I've seen her cry, sometimes.

C. Why do you think your mother sent you here?

T. Because she had a bad report from school . . . it wasn't that bad anyway.

C. And what did the report say?

T. That I wasn't working properly, and was rude to teachers. Wasn't really.

C. What were you being rude about?

T. It was only one or two teachers.

C. What did they do, that you needed to be rude to them about?

C. One of them kept on, this PE teacher saying how important sport was to your life, and that sort of thing . . . and that you ought to be fit all the time. Well, I told him, that's all.

C. You told him. What did you say to him?

T. I told him he didn't know what he was talking about.

C. He doesn't know about your Dad?

T. I don't know. He's not interested, anyway. I told another teacher she didn't know what she was talking about, too. That was in religious knowledge.

C. What did she say that you're angry about?

T. She said . . . we were talking about different religions and how some religions have been persecuted through the years, like the Jews, and I was trying to say that you don't have to be Jewish or anything to be persecuted. She didn't know what I meant. She wasn't listening.

C. Do you feel Dad and you are being persecuted?

T. Well, something's happening, isn't it? Everybody's against us. Well, not against us, but don't understand us. Because we're not like other people any more. Not a proper family any more.

C. Tim, do you agree, you're angry and hurt about the situation? And yet you still won't talk to anyone about it.

T. Who is there to talk to? When you try they shut you up, say you're being rude or . . .

C. Well, telling your PE teacher he's wrong, without telling him what your thinking is . . . Usually if people keep fit and healthy, they don't become ill like your father.

T. Some people do.

C. Some people do. And your PE teacher was talking about the majority of people.

T. He said all people. Well, that's what I think he said . . . twit, anyway.

C. So nobody wants to listen to you, and yet you don't ask anybody to.

T. Who could I ask?

C. You could ask your Mum?

T. She's too busy. She's got a lot to do . . . got to work, come home and do things, and she's got Dad to worry about.

C. I think she'd want to listen, if she knew all this was going on with you.

T. I don't know what you mean by 'all this going on' anyway.

C. The fact that you're hurt.

T. Of course I'm hurt, my Dad's . . . hardly my Dad any more. Well, he is, but he's not the same as he was. He's different.

C. And that make you different?

T. Sort of. Makes the whole family different. I don't know anyone else that's got a Dad like that.

C. And you're hurt, you're angry, and you're blaming other people.

T. No, I'm not. It's not anybody else's fault. It's not my fault, either.

C. No, I didn't say it was anyone's fault. But you get angry with teachers, and are rude to teachers, you're blaming them.

T. That's only because they won't . . . don't understand, take any notice of what you're saying.

C. Were you direct and clear about what you were saying?

T. Well, I'm . . . I've got a right to my point of view, anyway.

C. You certainly have. And you could start by going to a teacher that you respect and saying 'Could I have ten minutes of your time?'

T. I wouldn't know what to say if I did.

C. The same things that you're saying to me, now.

T. Anyway, they're always in lessons, or in the staff room, or with other teachers or something. Can't see them alone.

C. So you can find lots of reasons for their not being available to . . .

T. Yes.

C. There have to be lots of reasons why Mum and Dad aren't available. Mum's too busy, you told me, Dad's got too much on his plate at the moment.

T. Well, they have, both of them. Both got too much . . .

C. They also have time for you, Tim, if you ask them.

T. How can I? It's not me that's ill. Its Dad. Mum doesn't have to look after me. She doesn't have to worry about me; I'm not ill.

C. No, you're not ill, and you're very important to them.
T. I didn't say I wasn't.
C. You're acting as if you're not.
T. It's just that we're different now. We're different from anyone I know. I don't know any kids whose Dad's like my Dad. Used to be able to go to school and say, 'My Dad's in New York' or Hong Kong or whatever. Now all I can do is go to school and shut up.
C. What's frightening about talking to your Mum and Dad?
T. It's not frightening, they're just too busy. Well, Mum is, and Dad's not well enough.
C. So you've thought out reason after reason for not talking to him?
T. Only one. Dad's not well, that's all it is. I've got to put up with it.
C. What do you think is going to happen at school, Tim, over the next few months?
T. I don't know.
C. Guess.
T. Don't care much. I might change schools.
C. How are you going to organise that? By being rude? So that they kick you out?
T. Well, it doesn't matter. Coptfold School's better.
C. Have you talked this over with your parents?
T. No.
C. So you're going to get yourself expelled?
T. Well, Coptfold School's nearer home, anyway.
C. You're very, very tense, Tim.
T. No I'm not.
C. Just look at your hands.
T. Well, I've got . . . shall we go now?
C. Are you ready to go?
T. I said I'd be home by three o'clock.
C. What do you want to do about talking to your Mum?
T. Well, I'm not going to make any special arrangements, I'm not going to make an appointment to see my own mother.
C. That's good.
T. If she wants to come and talk to me, she can.
C. And you don't want to risk asking her, is that what you're saying?
T. Well, if I ask, and she's too busy, what then?
C. Well, you say, 'then when, Mum?'
T. Well, how can she know when she's not going to be busy or too tired? She doesn't know today if she's going to be tired tomorrow, nobody does.
C. You could let her know, Tim, that it's important.
T. I'm not going to make appointments with her. She's not a doctor or something — a dentist.
C. Well, Tim, I think it would be alright to go now, Tim, if you don't feel like talking any longer.

T.   Well, I'll stay if you want me to. I ought to be home by three o'clock, though. Have I got to come again?

C.   I think you can decide that between you and your mother.

T.   Why her?

C.   Well, it was an arrangement between the two of you.

T.   No, it wasn't. Between you and her.

C.   She asked me if I'd see you, Tim, and I said I would.

T.   Well, that's between you and her. Have I got to come again?

C.   What do you think?

T.   All right, I'll come next week, then.

C.   OK. I'll be delighted to see you, Tim. Same time?

T.   Yes. I'm going now.

C.   OK. Take care of yourself.

T.   Bye.

DISCUSSION

The initial impression with which Peter was left after role-playing Tim, was the strength of Tim's anger and sadness.

'For a time it felt like a sentimental sort of sadness, but . . . but as it went on it changed, and it felt more deep, real sadness.'

'As it went on it felt different, like I . . . I'd really lost something'.

The Counsellor then commented on how she had felt in her role.

'My thinking was, at the time, that I wasn't going to go in. It wasn't in the first session to go in-depth with someone who felt he was there under duress'.

'I would let you know that feeling sad was OK, and that you had a right to be angry.'

Some discussion followed as to whether this came across, and it is useful to look back at the transcript to see how Counsellor gave Tim permission to have feelings of sadness and anger.

Tim, describing his Dad's illness, said, 'It isn't fair'.

Counsellor asked what was not fair, and Tim answered with considerable feeling. Counsellor picked up the hurt in his voice, and asked, 'Does it hurt? That he can't be fun any more?'

Tim's reply is angry — ostensibly angry at Counsellor's 'silly question' — and when Counsellor comments on the sound of anger in his voice, Tim begins to discuss his anger, and his sadness.

Tim had felt that he had permission to be angry, and, in fact, had cried despite his strong feeling that 'Big boys don't cry'. He was not aware at a conscious level, however, of Counsellor letting him know that feeling sad was OK, and that he had a right to be angry.

Counsellor's recognition of the feelings behind what Tim was saying, her reflection of his statements, seem to have allowed Tim to talk about things he felt unable to talk about at school or at home.

Peter confirmed that Tim had found Counsellor a safe person to talk to, and to whom he could disclose his feelings, when we were talking about Tim's request to come again. His actual words were, 'Have I got to come again?' which sounds unlike what Peter describes as 'Tim's determination to come back again', but Gill described Tim's body language at this point. The body language said very clearly that it was of the utmost importance to Tim to be able to come back again.

'You didn't actually alter your posture until she said OK. You stayed firmly laced together. You brought your hands in front of your knees.' (Tim was sitting on the floor) 'And then you put your hands on your knees again. You were — you were very firmly tied up until you actually had a lead, that 'Yes' you know, you could come again if you liked, and then you slammed your hands down and were obviously prepared to go — no, you were absolutely determined you were not going to go without that opening.'

In fact, throughout the time Tim was saying such things as 'shall we go now?' and 'I said I'd be home by three o'clock', he was sitting with his arms wrapped firmly round his knees making no attempt to move or prepare to move. This was a statement that clearly belied, and was far stronger than, his apparent wish to end the interview and his stated indifference as to whether or not he was to return.

Gill remarked on the difference to Tim's picture of his father that the illness had made.

'Before the illness you came from a family that was different, because your Dad went to New York and all those other places, and came back and brought you presents and told you travel stories. *Now* you're different, so you've not just come down from having a Dad who's like everyone else . . .'

Peter confirmed and re-defined that.

'You were saying we've gone from different to different, I think we've gone from *special* to different.'

Ben felt deprived of this role as a man and as a father. We found it interesting the extent to which the loss of his father in a male role stereotype affected Tim. Counsellor felt that Tim was saying that his once all-exciting father was now pretty useless. She pointed out what the PE teacher had appeared to be telling Tim.

'He's telling you that men are *well*, and all *men* are well, a reminder again that you're different, your Dad is different.'

Tim's confusion, we felt, was focused by these conflicts over messages that he was getting from his teachers, that keeping fit as a boy will ensure health as a man, and in his religious knowledge lesson — that people are only persecuted on religious grounds — and his strong feelings that no one is to blame, it is no one's fault. He is sure that there is no time to talk about his needs and that nobody will understand his feelings, especially as he cannot understand them himself.

Tim seems to be concerned that someone ought to bear the blame for his father's illness and his own misery, but is unable to find that person, or anyone to whom to direct his anger.

He says, 'You can't be angry with someone that can't help what's happening.'

This could also be interpreted as a plea for Tim himself. His bad report, the complaints of rudeness to teachers, his apparent rejection by his parents, could all be interpreted by a nine-year-old boy as anger directed against him. He cannot help being disturbed and miserable about what has happened to him. He cannot help hitting out. Is he perhaps making a plea that people ought not to be angry with him when he says, 'You can't be angry with someone that can't help what's happening.'

Tim seems to have fairly clear ideas about what he imagines is expected of boys and girls, men and women. These stereotypes have given Tim, who now has a father at home doing the household tasks, not working and not being strong and able, a deeply disturbed view of the world. He feels unable to express the feelings aroused. He feels that he is not allowed to talk to his father and that his mother is too busy. His teachers do not understand.

He cannot feel angry — but he does.

He cannot cry — 'you've got to be strong,' 'It doesn't matter if girls cry, does it?' — but he wants to, needs to, cry.

The value of this counselling session to Tim, when he was able to express some of his anger, his sadness and his confusion, was made apparent by his determination to come back again.

TRANSCRIPT OF INTERVIEW WITH JEAN

(C = Counsellor, J = Jean)

C. Hello, Jean.

J. Organised myself a whole half hour, that's quite an achievement.

C. You've been very busy.

J. I function better being busy, I always have. Tim seemed to be, to have been OK when he came. He said you want him to come and see you again. Is that all right? It seems a bit of a funny position to land you in.

C. Jean, I said I'd be delighted to see Tim if he wants to come. I didn't tell him to come back, I wouldn't.

J. Well he certainly seems to want to.

C. Good.

J. You're sure that's all right?

C. Quite all right with me, but I do think it's important that it's his choice.

J. That's fine. That's one worry off my back, if I know he's got someone to talk to. He's a bit like Ben, really, he's always been very . . . very . . . oh, contained. I suppose we never had many bothers to talk about, really, you know, things at school, if he's got into the football team, so forth. He's a fairly . . . you know, self-possessed sort of person really. Like his father used to be.

C. What did you want to talk about? How did you want to use the time today?

J. I suppose to . . . to know if I'm doing the right thing. You know, I mean, when Ben was first ill, there were so many things that were obvious, that had to be done. There were an awful lot of practical things that had to be sorted out. He obviously wasn't going to be able to keep on with his job, and there were all sorts of financial things to consider, and the household to organise, and all that sort of thing, and . . . well, now it sometimes seems as though that's all running along beautifully, and well, what do I do next? I don't know. We . . don't seem to talk about it much, I . . .

C. Who's 'we', Jean?

J. Well, Ben and. . . we don't really talk about it much, I . . .

C. What do you and Ben talk about?

J. Well, I don't know, I . . . I mean, it seems like his whole life revolves around hospital and, you know, sometimes it seems that he'd rather talk about anybody but himself. I can understand that. What is there to talk about?

C. Do you have feelings about that? About his life revolving around the hospital?

J. Well, he's got to have something, hasn't he? and I'm glad really that he's got that interest. It seems . . it sometimes seems a bit depressing, the sort of people he seems to take an interest in, but . . you know, but at least it's an interest.

C. And is Ben attentive to you when you talk?

J. Oh I . . . I talk about my job, and so on. I was very lucky and I suppose I'm enjoying it more than I thought I would.

C. Does Ben show enough interest in you, Jean, and what you're doing?

J. Well, yes, I have to be careful; obviously I find myself enthusing about the job, to try and make him feel better, you know. He was very concerned at first, whether I'd be able to manage with looking after the children and the housework that he can't cope with. I try to reassure him by talking about the job, and sometimes think oh it's always me, sort of, talking about all the excitement of going up to town and everything, and that's not open to him any more, and I sometimes wonder just what I should be talking about, what would be best for him.

C. So if you get too excited or exuberant about what you are doing . . .

J. Oh, that's rubbing it in, isn't it?

C. Is it?

J. It really is, yes.

C. Have you asked if it feels that way to him?

J. Well, you know, right at the beginning he cried and he seemed . . . he seemed to fccl so ashamed at having done that . . . that I've made sure that . . . that it hasn't happened again because he seemed to find it worse having cried than whatever it was that made him cry.

C. Did he find it worse, or did you find it worse?

J. Well, somebody's got to be the strong one, haven't they? I think it would be OK now; I think I could let him cry and talk about it now, but now he won't.

C. How do you know, Jean?

J. Well . . . well, you know, I find sort of in bed, when the children are asleep . . .and, talking . . . I think there could be time then when we could talk about what he feels like, but then he seems to need so much reassurance that all that side of things isn't very important any more, you know, he'd sort of had so much . . . taken away from himself, that he needs so much reassurance, that I . . . I really don't mind, just being close and having each other is all right. And, I think he really needs to know that, and we tend to sort of talk about that more.

C. Do you ever tell him that you miss him, miss talking to him?

J. But we do talk. We talk about things that matter.

C. Feelings?

J. Well, you know, I know when things are worrying him. I try and reassure him, I think quite successfully most of the time. I don't mean I'm pretending. I don't mean I'm telling him lies — he knows me too well to get away with that — but it's . . . oh, you know, the sort of little things women do . . . pretty fragile in that sort of area, and I do no more than I would if I'm tired or not in the mood. You know, if you love someone that's part of it, isn't it?

C. Still, sex isn't satisfying, or as satisfying as it used to be?

J. Well, it just isn't really possible, not the way it used to be . . . Ben gets . . . too tired or can't really manage. But, you know, then he thinks I'm missing out, and I have to sort of reassure him that I'm not. I know he feels very bad about it, and I just like to reassure him about that.

C. So you miss your old sex life.

J. Oh well, yes, because that was something he taught me. I mean, I learned a lot from him. He used to tease me, say how he'd picked up his expertise on his travels round the world — that was a sort of joke we used to have, we used to have lots of jokes about that — and . . . you know . . . of course, we miss that . . . it's one of the things you have to accept, really.

C. How do you feel about it?

J. Well, I miss it.

C. You felt that?

J. Well, yes of course . . . We've found a way of coping with it.

C. What else do you feel sad about, Jean?

J. Well, I feel sorry for Ben . . . seeing him pottering around . . . oh, I have to absolutely bite my tongue sometimes when I see him doing ridiculous things with the ironing, and well, I just sort of do them again when he's at the hospital. And I think that's the thing that worries me most, I find myself getting so angry with Ben. And, that's just not fair, because he's really doing the best he can, well, you know, most of the time I just bite my tongue. But when I don't — could bite my tongue out sometimes when I snap at him . . . I don't do it often, it just comes out sometimes, you know . . .

C. It's understandable to me, that you'd be angry about changes in your life, the fact that Ben was different — before.

J. Well yes, I mean you never think it's going to happen to you. We got married in church, saying 'for better, for worse', and 'in sickness and in health', and I suppose you mean them when you say them all, you don't really expect that it's going to happen to you. When it does happen, it sort of knocks you sideways for a bit, you know, it's something that happens to the whole family, lots of . . . well, you know, you have a sort of plan ahead of you, how the children are growing up, and the things you're going to do, you know. We had Tim and Susie quite young, and Ben was in a very good job, so, you know, you've got a bit of savings too . . . we would have been young enough to travel a bit. Ben wanted to show me places he's been.

C. So there is loss about the things you're not going to have together.

J. Well, yes, almost literally.

C. And how about your feelings?

J. Well, I don't really believe he's going to *die*, but I know that he could. Yes, but I mean, he could, they explained at the hospital; they were very good. I don't know how much they told Ben . . . we always did have his insurance up-to-date with all his travel, silly little things, you know. It's come out of the back of the filing cabinet, it's in the top desk drawer. I mean, I'm not really sure I really knew where it was. I couldn't talk about that.

C. You're being very strong and coping, Jean, and now you're saying you don't want to feel your feelings too much? And I felt that in Tim as well, that you were being very strong and coping, coping against future odds.

J. Well, it's . . . I try to talk, talk to Tim, to reassure him.

C. What were you reassuring him about?

J. Perhaps Ben could talk to Tim.

C. Does Ben ever ask you about feelings?

J. I think . . . he's got enough to cope with. He's got to know that we can manage.

C. Jean, are you aware of how you're clutching your cup? You seem quite frightened, holding it all together.

J. Well, you know, at the moment . . . I can't help holding it together . . . I'm not trying to make him feel that I'm taking his responsibilities away from him, it's really important that he still feels the man of the family and so on, but I'm just holding it together, that's all . . . making him still feel important. I mean he is important . . . he thinks he is important, you know, it's just some of the practical details that he can't . . . can't manage, and you can't always be the practical one in the family.

C. You must be having feelings about the changes — what he's not able to do any longer.

J. It's awful to watch him. You know, sometimes when I think about him, have him in my mind, it's the old Ben . . . and it's almost every time he comes in, it's like . . . like knowing it all over again, because I expect to see him coming through the door, and then when I actually see him, it's all a bit of a shock. I hear people tell me how much better he is . . . how well he's looking and how well he's doing. I don't know what they're talking about because, you know, you have this sort of picture of somebody . . .

C. Of how he was?

J. Of how he was, and it's the car screeching up outside the house, and it's Ben — you know I always got the impression that he got out without opening the car door [laughs]. He can't really have done, but that's what it felt like. And coming up the steps, you know, sort of dropping things behind him and so on. I mean . . . and, I mean, well just sort of taking over the whole house, fluorescent lighting everywhere, everything just lit up. And when I hear his key in the door, that's what I'm expecting to see, and I . . . I . . .

C. . . . and feel that excitement again . . .

J. . . . then I hear him fumbling and . . . and . . . I'm afraid I'm just never . . . never going to get used to that.

C. Jean, you won't get used to it unless you acknowledge that you have strong feelings about the situation, and about what was, and what is now. You know, a major strain on you is your holding things together.

J. I'm not going to be able to hold things together if I'm sitting at home crying, am I?

C.   Crying again. You're going to have these feelings a lot. A person has changed dramatically. Usually it's difficult to resolve if you don't acknowledge that.

J.   I just don't feel that's going to solve anything.

C.   We're not talking about what happened to Ben, we're talking about you.

J.   Yes, well, I've got . . . got to stay together to help him. I know that sounds as if I'm saying I'm indispensable, I know, but there just isn't anyone else to hold the family together. There isn't anyone else who knows how Ben really feels. Then they've got this picture of him at the hospital; they're always saying how wonderful he is, how marvellously he's taken it, and how good he is with the other patients. And they don't know what it's really like for him. I've got to be there and I've got to be the same for him. If I change, then he's got nothing. He's got nothing left at all. The only thing he's got is me. And if I don't understand, nobody's going to understand.

C.   Jean, I want to tell you something about Tim. And that is that Tim is suffering a lot, Tim hurts a lot, and one of the ways that you can help Tim is by letting him share what you feel, and therefore letting Tim share what is going on within him. But he's holding it all together himself, too. Like you're doing for the rest of the family. And Tim really needs to talk about his feelings in the family.

J.   Well, certainly, I . . . I feel badly about Tim. I will do as you say, let him talk.

C.   Do you think *you'll* get anything out of that, Jean?

J.   Well, I'm really glad that he's told you that, or that you've found that out. I do feel that I've pushed him a bit aside. Someone outside can see where I've gone wrong, I'm glad you saw that and told me.

C.   Jean, I didn't say you were going wrong.

J.   Well, no . . . all right, you didn't exactly say that.

C.   No, I didn't say that. I said, what can you give for either of you to be able to talk about what's going on, what your feelings are about the situation?

J.   I can . . . I can help him, I can tell him, you know . . . I'll try and find a way of doing it . . . try to talk to him about it. But it's got to be the right time. I mean, that might be something Ben could do for Tim, that would be good . . . that would be something . . . that would be good for Ben . . . But I'm not going to break.

C.   No way.

J.   No way. I couldn't.

C.   No way. No *way*.

DISCUSSION

Gill came partly out of the role at the end of the session, feeling very strongly that Jean was quite determined not to lower her defences and disclose her real feelings, to someone towards whom she felt a certain degree of resentment.

Counsellor was fully aware of how Jean was feeling, and in the ensuing discussion Gill said, referring to Tim, '. . . he's found somebody and somewhere to talk and I haven't — I haven't. I knew damn well I wasn't going to let you get under my cover, I mean, that was the battle for . . . the whole way through'.

Peter felt strongly that Jean was enjoying the power she held, and that her demands on Ben before the illness would have been impossible for Ben to continue to live up to.

'This wonderful guy who came down with the fluorescent lights', 'This idealised bit about you and Ben going off into the sunset hand in hand.'

The picture of the family that Jean was describing was of Jean as 'the big master' with Tim as a 'small man', 'Susan's my child' (these are Peter's comments). Gill, in the role of Jean, added, 'Susie's *my* child.'

Counsellor agreed and added, 'Ben I think now became the third child. You're parenting him, reassuring him about everything.'

The effect of this parenting of Ben by Jean is apparently, as Gill commented, 'Castrating him far more effectively than if I had complained about his inability.'

The interview with Jean certainly confirmed for us Ben's feelings and Tim's dilemma. What, however, had Jean wanted? Had she got it?

(P = Peter, G = Gill, C = Counsellor.)

P.   I wonder why she came?

G.   Evaluation . . . I think.

C.   Well, OK, I asked her. She said, 'I want to know if I'm doing the right thing.'

P.   For Tim? Or for everybody?

G.   Well, for everybody.

C.   I think, for everybody. Yes. And then she promptly went about setting it up so I'd kick her about, neglecting Tim, that she would see me as kicking her about her imperfection.

This 'setting up' where Jean chose to hear Counsellor's suggestion that Tim seemed to feel he was 'holding it all together' just as Jean did, as criticism, and Counsellor's suggestion that for Jean to share with Tim how she was feeling in order to help both of them, as condemnation, is interesting. What motive can Jean have in apparently wanting to feel criticised?

We felt that Jean was getting a degree of satisfaction about what was happening to her family.

In the discussion, Gill said, 'I think I knew all along that women really ran the Universe, but there was quite an affirmation for me, that in my little family it was being approved.'

So Jean, whom Counsellor describes as 'a controlling and managing woman', is actually enjoying coping in a situation where her controlling and managing powers can be seen as nothing but admirable. She has coped, the family is outwardly successful, surviving appalling catastrophe and Jean can see herself as the heroine of the drama.

We are not suggesting that Jean's feelings were conscious, or that Jean did not feel acutely all the disappointment, strain and fears that she expressed to Counsellor. We do suggest that out of the whole family, the effect of Ben's illness gave Jean the opportunity of expressing her need to be in control.

Tim having told Counsellor that he 'is suffering a lot, hurts a lot', threatens Jean's picture of herself as in control and managing all the family successfully. Because Counsellor has told her this, Jean needs to see Counsellor as unfairly critical. Therefore she tries to put Counsellor in the wrong.

'I just wanted to make you feel bad for criticising me. How could you, you know, be so dreadful and pick up the one little thing I wasn't doing right?'

We all felt that Jean needed her excellent defences so much that counselling her would be a long process, almost a lifetime's work. Her visit to Counsellor was really to reassure herself as to her own rightness, not to consider the possibility of any change.

So what would be the role of the counsellor in such a case?

Remembering the definition of client-centred counselling as 'enabling a client to recognise and identify his own problems and to find his own solution or resolution', our interpretation of the dynamics of Jean's role in her family should not — must not — form an agenda for how counselling 'should' proceed.

Should Jean request counselling (and she was very clear at the end of her session with Counsellor that she would make *no* such request), the course of such counselling would be Jean's to direct. The role of the counsellor would be to help Jean to become aware of what she is saying, of the feelings that she seems to be expressing. Should Jean then wish to work on any problems that she perceives, the counsellor will help her to do this.

As far as counselling for Ben, Tim and Susie is concerned, Counsellor felt that Tim would probably be the 'identifying client' through whom the family could acknowledge that help was needed. Tim's disturbed behaviour at school and his bad report, would have been fairly clear indications of problems that needed outside help.

Peter and Gill pointed out that Ben had also attempted to ask for help directly, by discussing with his social worker a patient with whose plight Ben felt some identification.

What is apparent is that all the members of the family, not excluding Susie (who seems to be possessively 'my problem' for Jean), need help. This help is needed both individually and as a family to resolve the very considerable difficulties that Ben's disabilities have created.

It is a sad fact that there are few people with both counselling skills and experience in disability available to such a family. Or is it that there are few people with experience in disability and illness who are willing to risk recognising, extending and using their counselling skills — and vice versa?

5.

SELF-AWARENESS

We have suggested that one of the prerequisites to learning counselling skills is a degree of self-awareness.

Our emotional reactions colour and sometimes confuse our perception of life, our response to other people and our ability to form relationships and make decisions. Those emotional reactions are influenced by many factors, including early experience of success or failure, acceptance or rejection.

The expectations and demands of those among whom we spend our early years, experiences from which we have learned a response or strategy, and further experiences that seem to have confirmed or resulted in modification of that response, all influence what we may imagine is a reaction of logic rather than emotion.

TRANSACTIONAL ANALYSIS (TA)

The model of the dynamics of relationships referred to as Transactional Analysis recognises a number of ego-states in the adult personality. These ego-states have evolved during a person's development and an adult can function in all or any of these states. The first ego-state common to everyone is the new-born condition of Free Child. A neonate is a person of pure and immediate emotion. He feels what he feels, and his reactions are immediate and unequivocal. He will, in various situations, feel pain, rage, joy, fear, satisfaction and every other emotion and his whole consciousness is involved in their expression.

The Free Child is not, however, in this state of total ego consciousness for long. He will experience parenting in some form, either from his parents or from temporary or long-term parent-substitutes.

The Nurturing Parent is the parent who accepts the Free Child as he is. The Nurturing Parent can offer approval, acceptance and support. The Nurturing Parent can protect the Child. However, Free Child does not remain unchanged by this parenting. His relationship with the Parent is one of interaction. The Nurturing Parent is aware of the necessity of the Child to modify some of his behaviour in order for him to take an acceptable part in the community in which he lives and to protect him from harm. Without rejecting the Child, the Nurturing Parent will indicate strategies that will enable the Child to become more acceptable, gain approval, in the community. Of course, these may sometimes be ill-judged or not really appropriate.

The Critical Parent conveys to the Child that he, Free Child, is not acceptable as he is. The Critical Parent lays down norms of behaviours, acceptable reactions, and indicates that rejection or disapproval will be the result of deviation from these imposed demands.

Thus Adapted Child emerges. Adapted Child is well aware that his instinctual and immediate reactions may bring isolation and lose him love, and adapts his behaviour to what he sees as the demands of those on whom he is dependent for his emotional as well as physical needs.

This process is, of course, gradual and continuous. Our responses are in a state of continual modification according to the situation in which we live and work, but very often many of our responses are those of a child adapted by a parent in the very early stages of our development. This state can sometimes lead to inappropriate perceptions of our social interactions and block our ability to grow and develop.

An example may clarify this statement.

It was a fairly common demand in the middle-class South of England home that a child's anger be suppressed. A child expressing anger faced rejection or punishment, so learned an alternative strategy. A safe strategy would ideally be one that not only avoided rejection, but one that was rewarded. In the society referred to, tears were often interpreted as proper remorse, and a weeping child would be comforted. A child who had expressed anger and was crying from fear and anticipation of punishment might well then be cuddled and consoled. Thus, a child could soon learn to express the emotion of anger in the currency of another emotion entirely, that of grief. Instead of experiencing rejection he could earn love, or so it appeared to him. Each confirmation of this served to reinforce this adapted behaviour.

Such an adaptation, learned and fixed in early life and then continually reinforced, would persist into adult life. It could then be totally inappropriate and could block the person's ability to function effectively. When, for example, someone justifiably angry at an unfair situation is unable to confront the author of his misfortunes and use his anger to justify his case, but instead risks, or fears the risk of, bursting into tears, his adapted behaviour is not acting to his advantage.

The ego states described, Free Child, Adapted Child, Nurturing and Critical Parents, can all be integrated into the adult personality. Each person has access to the strengths of his various ego-states. Each person is vulnerable to their weaknesses.

Free Child holds the creativity of anger and aggression, the joy of love, the release of grief. Free Child has, however, no judgement or control.

The Parents have control and information, but Critical Parent can be repressive and rejecting, blocking spontaneity and creativity. Nurturing Parent can provide love and acceptance but may inhibit the chances of taking risks and making choices.

Adapted Child can learn and profit from experience but may be fearful and pessimistic and fail to recognise what is offered.

If the adult is aware of the ego-states operating within his personality, and is aware of their development in his life, he can deliberately use their strengths and operate in the ego-state or states most appropriate for the result he wishes to obtain.

If he is unaware, then responses learned long ago and often no longer appropriate may block and prevent him from realising his full potential as a reactive, interactive adult, in charge and responsive.

For example, fear may be an appropriate and life-saving response. On the other hand, fear may prevent a person from ever taking any positive decisions or experiencing freedom of choice.

Exercises using transactional analysis

It is possible to begin to identify the ego-states operating in a particular transaction or relationship, and to judge their appropriateness, with practice.

Think of a recent situation in which you felt anger or regret that you were somehow prevented from handling it effectively.

Identify the feelings that prevented you. Were they fear, sadness, inadequacy? If it is not at once obvious, re-enact the scene in your mind. Become aware of your body when doing this. Are your fists clenched? Is there a lump in your throat? Are you shaking? These may give you clues.

Now try to remember another occasion when you experienced the same feelings. Can you now place an occasion further back in your past? In your childhood?

Let yourself experience the feeling and be aware of the thoughts that come to you and the memories. If you cannot remember at once, keep trying. Return to the physical effect of the emotion. Your body may have a memory of an occasion that your conscious mind has forgotten, and reliving these feelings may unearth a buried memory.

When you have traced the feeling back to your earliest memories of it, you may well have given yourself a clue as to when and in what circumstances you originally learned the response that is blocking you as an adult. Consider this carefully. That response was once a useful one. Is it serving any useful purpose now? Is your adult self benefiting from that adaptation?

It is likely that a fairly clear decision can be made. It is equally likely that the decision will be that this particular adaptation is not only inappropriate, it is positively harmful.

It is at this point that the strengths of Nurturing Parent can be called on. It will be necessary to reassure yourself that to deliberately unlearn a piece of behaviour is not only possible but can be beneficial.

You can practise. Imagine yourself back in the original scene which started this exercise. Imagine yourself reacting in a way that is appropriate to the sort of person you really are. What will happen? What is the worst thing that could happen?

Could you cope with that? Remember the strengths you have to call on, the ego-states that are accessible to your adult self.

Such an experience may sound simplistic, or even eccentric. There are many people who carry on such dialogues within themselves. We may deliberately personify Nurturing Parent or Free Child at times of stress when we need their strength and reassurance. We can testify how enabling such exercises can be.

TRANSACTIONS

The same tactics can be applied to transactions with other people, identifying in which ego-state they are operating and how we are responding.

Certain ego-states are interactive. One person taking the role of Critical Parent almost invariably results in the response of Adapted Child. This is a common strategy used, consciously or unconsciously, by those in authority when dealing with subordinates.

This pattern is not, however, inevitable. It is not necessary to produce the interactive response. The transaction can be changed by an awareness of the tactics. A response made deliberately from the adult, or from one of the Parent ego-states, can foil the intended ploy. Equally, to initiate the transaction and consciously establish the roles you desire will often be effective.

BEHAVIOUR MODIFICATION

A useful set of considerations, when a pattern of behaviour in ourselves has been identified and we wish to change it, is contained in the following sequence of questions.

What do I want to be able to do?

What would be the benefits to me?

What will I have to change in myself?

What will I have to change around me?

How will I try to prevent myself from changing?

The last question may need explanation; change is almost always threatening. The unknown can seem more threatening than even the most unsatisfactory present.

We are all expert at rationalising our failure to act, and it is wise to look out for the phenomenon known as 'Yes, but'. Should you have defined an unsatisfactory pattern of behaviour and have begun to find ways of changing, you may well find that your ideas are being blocked by apparently logical and insurmountable objections, 'Yes, but if I do that . . .'

If you recognise this ploy but still find your own objections overwhelming, then you need to query whether you do indeed want to change. You may be trying to change too much, or too soon. You may not really want to change and are preventing yourself by finding rational reasons. You may want to change but fear is causing you to find reasons not to.

Another way we prevent change in ourselves is by procrastination. We will find excellent reasons for not starting to change today. 'Next week — once this particularly stressful time is over', 'when I feel better', 'when I have had time to explain to someone else what I am doing', are all examples of typical preventing ploys.

If we can anticipate these, their power is much reduced.

GESTALT AWARENESS EXERCISES

An integrated personality depends on all of its parts interacting to form a coherent whole. When one aspect of a person's development fails to be integrated successfully and prevents a balanced picture by impinging upon the background, then the gestalt or wholeness of that person is incomplete.

Dys-integration of one aspect of a personality may be caused by a failure to recognise, work through and resolve some conflict or difficulty in the past. This 'unfinished business', this unacceptable and unaccepted tension, can so unbalance a personality as to render relationships difficult and action irresolute.

The discovery — or rather recovery — of incidents that have caused this imbalance, can by their recognition and remembrance be integrated. Similarly, a recognition of where an imbalance exists, without necessarily discovering its origin, can equally facilitate integration. It seems as if the act of identification is sufficient at a conscious level. The subconscious then seems able to complete the process of integration. The pain or fear that has been blocking action is resolved and the gestalt restored.

Working at a level where the explanation of what appears to happen is expressed symbolically, one finds that it is logical that some of the effective exercises in self-awareness are also symbolic.

Look around the room in which you are sitting. Choose any object in that room. Look at it closely.

Now describe that object in as great a detail as you can, but do this using the first person. Describe the object as if you were that object.

For example, a client disabled with rheumatoid arthritis was invited to choose an item from her home and describe it as if she were the article. She thought for a moment and then smiled broadly.

'I am a kitchen stool, a step stool,' she said. 'I am old and a bit battered but very serviceable. I am well-used and have my own place.'

Up to this point, her expression and voice had been warm and amused. Then she frowned slightly.

'I am kept in the kitchen but if anyone wants me I get dragged all over the house and used to help people climb up to reach things.'

Her voice became louder and a note of complaint crept in. Her frown deepened.

'They climb all over me with their heavy shoes and bang me back into my corner when they have finished with me. I get chipped and . . and bruised and no-one notices, I'm just there when they need me but no-one really thinks about how I feel . .'

She stopped abruptly, her voice breaking and tears in her eyes. The cheerful, philosophical, coping and practical woman had for the first time begun to express her anger and grief at the major change in her life caused by her illness and the inability of her family to understand. Her next task involved exploring why she had made such efforts to conceal her feelings from her family. The kitchen stool, however, facilitated a breakthrough in the counselling process.

The choice of the kitchen stool appeared arbitrary. After all, she had been asked to choose *anything* in her home to describe. Perhaps subconsciously she recognised the potential of that piece of furniture as an enabler for her to express deep feelings. Perhaps anything she chose would have 'worked', the attributes that she subconsciously selected being indicative of what was uppermost in unresolved pain distorting her gestalt.

We would surmise that she chose the stool because of a subconscious recognition of its possibilities as a symbol to enable her to recognise her difficulty.

That recognition was painful. The client was distressed at what she felt were shameful feelings; she should not complain, her family did their best to help, she should be taking her illness in her stride.

Hidden and buried feelings have been concealed for a reason. Revealing them is therefore likely to be painful. However, the choice whether or not to reveal was the client's and she 'chose' to do so. She also chose to recognise and own those feelings and to continue to explore them.

The most valuable result of this deceptively simple exercise was the identification of messages received in childhood, messages she had learned well. These messages conveyed that she would please others by being cheerful, efficient and undemanding. She decided that these lessons were no longer helpful and that denying her own needs was costing her too much in suppressed anger and resentment — and the resulting guilt.

To change proved painful. However, many months later one of her teenage children confessed that to have a 'perfect' mother had imposed a nearly intolerable strain upon him; her husband proved able to (and happy to) sympathise and support, and the client reported that although life was more turbulent, with feelings expressed and arguments frequent, she felt that it was a much happier family. She felt it was a happy coincidence that her arthritis had improved somewhat at the same time.

We would query that particular coincidence!

We have used the present tense, and gestalt exercises take place in the present. The distortion, whatever its origin, is affecting the present.

It is in the present that it is expressed. The origin can be interesting, even helpful to understanding but, in the practical resolution of the unfinished nature of that particular piece of business, it is in the here and now.

A similar technique uses the waking memories of a dream.

It does not really matter if the memory is fragmented, or if the teller fears that he is embroidering or altering what he 'really' dreamt. The dream is a symbol and the subconscious will select what is useful.

A counsellor in supervision was experiencing problems with a particular client. The counsellor was severely disabled and the client an able-bodied man experiencing marital difficulties.

Her supervisor suggested that she record any dreams she had. The counsellor protested that she 'never dreamed' but agreed doubtfully that she would do as the supervisor suggested, if she had a dream.

A telephone call the following morning reported that a particularly vivid dream had occurred and had been duly written down. In supervision the next week the counsellor was asked to describe the dream, using the present tense.

She was in her bedroom in the dream, she said, redecorating, stripping the old, dirty and old-fashioned wallpaper from the walls. She was then pasting up fresh, new paper in sunny colours. Her supervisor was also there, helping, and together they chose new, modern furniture.

The counsellor enthusiastically interpreted the dream as being symbolic of her supervisory relationship, which she felt was enabling her to discard old, outdated ideas and feelings and choose new ways of being.

The supervisor asked the counsellor to speak as if she was the old wallpaper.

'I am old, used up, no longer any use. I need to be scraped off, thrown away. It hurts to be scraped off but there are lovely clean smooth walls underneath.'

The session continued: the scraper, the new wallpaper, the furniture — all confirmed the dreamer's interpretation. The supervisor did not express her intuitive feeling that all this elaborate symbolism was a decorative and convincing 'red herring' and that the real message was being concealed. The 'instruction' to the counsellor had been, in effect, to have a dream about the difficulties with her client. The supervisor waited and listened.

Nearly at the end of the session, when describing the room, the counsellor referred to 'the carpet rolled up at the back of the room.' The supervisor noted that this carpet had not been mentioned before: and also that its appearance had coincided with the end of the supervision session. She suggested that the counsellor spend a few minutes that evening 'being' the carpet and mentioned that she felt it could be pivotal to the whole dream.

The counsellor was sceptical but agreed, and the session ended.

At the next session, the counsellor seemed subdued and thoughtful. When the supervisor invited her to talk, she said.

'That *bloody* carpet. I think you're a witch.'

She thought for a minute, then announced,

'I am going to repeat what happened after I got home last week, when I spoke to myself as the carpet.

'OK, here it is.

'I am a carpet. I am green, but you can't see my colour because I have been rolled up out of the way. All the decorating going on, I am pushed to the back and ignored. I am getting covered in all this old wallpaper, hidden under it. I don't want to be rolled up here — *I wanna get layed*!'

The counsellor looked at the supervisor.

'Do you know what it means, to get layed? Do you know that expression?' she asked. The supervisor nodded and reflected, 'You want to get laid? To have sex?'

The counsellor responded angrily.

'Of course I do! What do you think? I'm normal, not some kind of sexless freak. Of course I do!'

'Don't you realise how difficult it is for me to talk to this man I'm supposed to be counselling about his sexual problems? I just wish I had his problems, even problems are better than nothing at all . . .'

In a long period of work with her supervisor the counsellor had never mentioned her feelings about her own sexuality and sexual needs. The supervisor had felt strongly that there were very powerful feelings of suppressed grief, anger and frustration that were blocking the counsellor's work with her client. She felt equally strongly that the counsellor would strenuously deny such feelings.

It seemed that even the counsellor's subconscious mind was involved in this denial; the dream was full of very valid symbolism that could have been constructively explored.

Only a passing reference at the very end of the session gave a clue to the disclosure that could be discovered. The supervisor's skill lay in her being open to her own feelings as to the validity of the images already explored and her attentiveness as to the content of the dream as it was explored.

The counsellor, of course, was free at a subconscious level to choose whether or not to allow recognition of the symbolism of the carpet to occur. The delightful punning statement 'I wanna get layed' is very typical of dream work when symbols may be almost mischievously disguised. It also, of course, provided a final choice as to whether or not the counsellor chose to recognise and own the punning allusion.

Subsequent work with the supervisor began the long process of resolution. At an early stage of this work the counsellor recognised that she was blocking empathy with her client. She then felt able to work constructively with him.

Self-awareness or the identification of our own reactions and emotional perceptions is an essential skill for a counsellor.

Various 'games' or exercises, a few of which we have described, can help heighten self-awareness.

When we become aware of aspects of ourselves we should like to change, we have the potential ability for conscious change.

That change is not achieved by attempting to suppress or deny negative elements, but by making a positive attempt to identify and integrate disturbing memories and encourage and accept positive attributes.

6.

BLOCKING STRATEGIES: SUPERVISION

When we undergo experiences which are emotionally distressing or disturbing, we have a number of strategies for dealing with these painful emotions.

Free Child will respond by immediately expressing the emotion. Free Child will scream with fear or anger, weep with grief or bereavement and howl with pain. The emotional distress is expressed, and when the incident is over the emotions engendered by it have been released and the experience is completed.

The reaction of a parent in this situation may at first be to comfort, to reassure, to accept the strength of the emotional reaction and to give as much reassurance and support as the child needs. However, it is the experience of most of us that such simple acceptance is soon modified, withdrawn. The expression of fear may be met with injunctions to be brave, not to be silly. Anger may not be accepted, any expression of anger may be met with punishment and adult anger. There may be attempts to distract a sobbing child with sweets or promises, or threatened or actual punishment.

The child may learn that to express some of the emotions he feels is not acceptable. He may learn to repress or modify his emotional response, to displace his feelings or to cut himself off from them.

This behaviour is rewarded by the approval of the parent and any success the child has in managing not to express his feelings is reinforced.

In many societies the expression of emotion, particularly anger or grief, is discouraged. The growing child learns that acceptability depends on its suppression and becomes skilled, to a greater or lesser degree, in achieving this.

For the Free Child, the emotion is expressed and released and once the precipitating situation is removed and the physical reaction to strong emotion calms, the incident is over. However, should the emotion not be expressed or the feelings suppressed, then the pain, fear, anger and grief remain, to be triggered off whenever anything occurs that is reminiscent of the original stimulus. These renewed emotions can in their turn be suppressed or displaced and the stress increased.

This process may have a profound effect on the functioning of a person in his everyday life.

When the pain of unexpressed feelings is not recognised or acknowledged then the subconscious may employ strategies to ensure that such recognition does not occur. These blocks will not be apparent to the conscious mind but will influence a great deal of the person's behaviour. A few examples may perhaps appear familiar.

A normally organised and efficient woman had to keep an appointment about which she felt nervous. She forgot the address, lost the piece of paper on which the directions were written and could not find the name in the telephone directory — although when she checked this after the interview (to which she eventually found her way) the name she had been seeking was clearly displayed.

A counsellor listening to a client talking about his sexual difficulties found that she was having great difficulty in concentrating. When making notes afterwards she found she could not remember much of what had been said.

A young woman several times forgot to keep a clinic appointment. She twice recalled that she had an appointment half an hour too late to be able to get there.

The first woman associated the particular interview with feelings of inadequacy and of being criticised. Authority was, to her, always likely to recall a demanding and critical father. She could not allow herself to recognise and experience this painful association and tried unconsciously to avoid any situation that would expose her hurt.

When she recalled with a counsellor childhood memories of criticism and failure and realised and felt the associations she was making, she was able to look clearly at the interview she had been avoiding. She was able as an adult to recognise that the interviewer was not her critical father and that she was not, if ever had been, a stupid and disobedient child. In fact, in the course of working with the counsellor this client was able to see that she had not been the stupid child she had always felt herself to be. Her initial feelings of anger about this early criticism caused her very great distress, and she was able to feel and express both the anger and grief and sense of loss that her discovery had caused her. Later, she was able to decide that her father's motives had been dictated by his wish to arm her for what he saw as a hostile world. She was able to make her peace with him and was enabled to cope with authority in a much more realistic way.

The counsellor had unresolved feelings regarding her own sexual identity. When the client's disclosures began to come uncomfortably close to her own painful areas she attempted subconsciously to protect herself by not hearing or remembering what the client had said.

In supervision the counsellor was able to use her recognition of a block in order to discover the nature of that block and from there to work on resolution of her own difficulties.

The young woman had a deep and largely unacknowledged fear of serious illness, suppressed through guilt. This guilt was associated with enjoying illness as a child because being ill had 'earned' her the love and attention of her parents. This had led to an element of excitement that made the thought of illness in part attractive to her. She half recognised that serious illness would entitle her to the attention and caring that she did not find or feel able to ask for in her everyday life.

This painful conflict of guilt and need she attempted to ignore by 'forgetting' the appointment that might bring the conflict to the surface.

BLOCKS IN COUNSELLING

The stresses and confusions that can be caused by unacknowledged pain and the blocks that we set up, can be the cause of an inability to establish an open and creative partnership in the counselling relationship. When the blocks are the client's, the counsellor can, by reflection and confrontation, enable the client to begin to recognise, acknowledge and then work toward the resolution of the difficulties.

When it is the counsellor who is doing the blocking, a similar process is necessary. If the counsellor is aware of areas where she is experiencing uneasiness, or finds she is having problems in hearing what the client is saying, hard work is necessary on her part.

The supervisor is then the resource for the counsellor to explore her blocks in much the same way as has been indicated for the client. The counsellor may well be able to work on her own problems to a considerable degree using exercises such as have already been described. First, though, there must be recognition and self-awareness. Perhaps, most importantly, there must be acceptance of self.

Warmth and reassurance for the client have been described as part of the counsellor's role. It is equally important for the counsellor, as for all of us, to receive warmth and reassurance.

We shall probably need to ask for this.

The client has asked when he approaches the counsellor. The client has assured himself of the gift of warmth and support in the counselling contract. Where does the counsellor receive this? Who can be asked?

Some of us have relationships in our own lives in which we feel able to ask for and free to receive what we need to satisfy our emotional needs. More commonly, we are reluctant to ask. We fear rejection, ridicule, lack of understanding, mere kindness or a dismissal of the importance of our need. We may fear that a reciprocal demand will be made that we are unable to fulfil. Such fears, some or all of which may be familiar, can prevent us asking even those we are close to.

We have said that we all need warmth and reassurance. For the counsellor in particular, involved with the pain and confusion of clients suffering from problems which may be intractable, that need is of vital importance.

In some instances it may be that the counsellor is working in total isolation. We feel that this is very far from ideal and would certainly not recommend it. Should this be the situation it is vital that it is remedied as soon as possible. The British Association for Counselling would be able to provide information about local accredited counsellors as well as groups, which it may be helpful to contact.

For the counsellor, counselling is a total involvement demanding a high expenditure of emotional energy.

A good supervisor can provide both a source of warmth and support and a resource for working on the dynamics of the counselling relationships with which the counsellor is engaged.

SUPERVISION

Where is this supervision to be found? It may be available as part of the working structure (see Chapter Seven).

A Team Leader, a member of a Group, a superior in the profession may be available and suitable as a potential supervisor. It may be possible to ask for supervision and to make a contract. This is in no way to imply that supervision must be from a superior. A colleague with counselling skills who is willing to make regular commitment may be your supervisor.

Outside the working structure, supervision may be sought from any counsellor or psychotherapist. In this case, a fee may need to be negotiated to contract for the time of the supervisor. The fixing of this fee usually forms part of the contract between the counsellor and the supervisor.

Co-counselling may be another way of obtaining supervision. Two counsellors may contract with each other for mutual supervision. The allocation of time should be contracted and a regular commitment made.

Some counsellors use a group for supervision. This group is not necessarily one in which the counsellor works professionally but may be a regular meeting of counsellors contracted to give each other supervision as a group. In this way of obtaining supervision the individual will need to assert her needs. The allocation of group time will need to be continually reviewed and renegotiated when necessary.

Wherever supervision is found, the contract between the counsellor and the supervisor needs to be very carefully and thoughtfully discussed. The needs of the counsellor and the skills of the supervisor need stating and the definition of supervision of both participants needs to be clarified. Considerable negotiation may be required before a mutually satisfactory agreement is reached.

Wherever supervision is found, however, it must be regarded as absolutely essential. We have no hesitation in stating that no counsellor should ever work with a client without first having arranged appropriate supervision.

ASSUMING THE ROLE OF COUNSELLOR

One of the unexpected difficulties encountered when the decision has been made to assume the role of counsellor, is in the expectations and assumptions of those we work and live among.

A fantasy may be defined as one person's interpretation of what he perceives as reality. It is the fantasy of many people that to be a counsellor is to be kind, nice, endlessly receptive and approving in every circumstance.

There may be the expectation that the counsellor is able to provide the answer to all problems. There is often the assumption that a counsellor is always available — or should be.

Other people's fantasies and expectations, imposed assumptions, can be very difficult to defend against. We are all imbued with the need to be seen as 'nice' and may, in fact, feel such a strong moral obligation to be a 'nice person' that we may make impossible demands on ourselves and feel guilty and inadequate when we inevitably fail.

A student on a course introducing counselling skills listened to a discussion among the course members. The group were talking about the decisions a counsellor needs to make when a clash of personalities, a frank dislike of a client, makes counselling that client seem impossible. She listened with an expression of disbelief, slowly changing to dawning relief.

'Are you really saying', she ventured, 'that we don't have to like everybody?'

The assumption that a counsellor must always be available and always responsive, the fantasy of an omnipresent fairy godmother, is one that puts impossible demands on anyone.

Most counsellors have encountered the client who makes numerous telephone calls, attempts to extend every session beyond the agreed time and becomes upset, angry and resentful should a counsellor insist on keeping to the contract.

All experienced counsellors know that one of the most difficult yet most valuable skills they have learned is that of saying no.

For me to assert my need for my own personal space is essential. I can only be an effective counsellor if I keep time for myself where I can fulfil my own needs and desires. I can only be a whole person if I give myself the consideration I need.

If I try to respond to everyone whenever they ask I shall become tired, resentful, and diminished. Neither shall I be helping my clients to value their own responsibilities in the counselling relationship. The contract has mutual responsibilities and if I allow the client to ignore his side of the contract I am denying his abilities. I will be assuming the role of Parent who is in charge and the director.

To learn to say no is difficult. It will be impossible if I have accepted the fantasy that a counsellor is some superhuman being with no needs of its own.

To return to the student. She believed that, as a counsellor, she must like everybody. This made it obvious that she must accept every client that asked for her skills. Apart from the obvious impossibility of allocating time to every potential client, the student was assuming that she would be able to counsel effectively any and every client.

While it is usually possible to empathise with most clients, there will be for every counsellor some areas where they are not able to accept the client's world. This may be a moral dilemma. Very strong feelings in the area of, say, sexual molestation of children may make it impossible for a counsellor to help a client. If the client wishes to change, to alter his practices and urges, some counsellors may feel able to work with him. Fewer counsellors would feel able to work with a client who wished to continue having sexual relationships with young children but wanted to rid himself of his feelings of guilt at so doing.

Counsellors need to make their own decisions regarding both moral and legal boundaries, and to decide where they will say no. To tell a client that a counsellor feels unable to help (because this is how the counsellor feels) may be difficult but is necessary for both counsellor and potential client. However, where possible the client should be referred to a person or agency where he may obtain help.

It is more difficult where the antipathy is less easy to define. One of the authors remembers the feeling of physical repulsion with a client who spat as she talked. Twenty years later the actual taste of her saliva on the bottom lip of the counsellor is remembered with a shudder. This may sound trivial, but such a problem can prevent the counsellor using her skills effectively and should be fully explored in supervision. The decision may be that the client would be better counselled by someone not vulnerable to that particular squeamishness.

While looking at the validity of others' fantasies, assumptions and expectations of the counsellor, we must not ignore our own. It may be a useful exercise to write our own definition of what a counsellor is.

We have found that a useful starting point is to take a statement that presents the common fantasy in a slightly exaggerated form.

'A counsellor should be like God — always there, knowing everything, always sympathetic, endlessly patient.'

This makes demands that are patently ridiculous. Attempting to modify this statement may make it easier to reach a definition that you find possible, acceptable and useful.

It may be pertinent at this point to remind the counsellor that a similar examination of her fantasies about the supervisor may be helpful to that relationship!

7.

WORKING STRUCTURES

Most professionals work in some kind of structure and with other people.

Three common structures, hierarchy, team and network, are expressed in Figure 7.1. We suggest that you identify your own position in the structure that seems closest to your own working conditions.

Fig. 7.1 Working structures

A *hierarchy* is the familiar pyramidal form of many organisations or departments within organisations.

The hierarchy in its most simple form consists of a leader and workers. More complex hierarchies involve a chain of command with a number of sections, sub-sections, departments or individuals, each being accountable to the next above in responsibility.

A *network* consists of a number of individual workers or collections of workers, each of which may have a nominal leader.

Each worker or collection of workers operates in an autonomous manner without support from, or responsibility towards, any other group or individuals within the network.

A *team* is a group of workers having individual responsibility, accountable to and for other members of the team.

A team may have a leader, who is responsible for the individuals in the team, and to whom the team members may be accountable.

When all members of a team, including the leader when there is one, accept the responsibility of supporting and sharing skills with every member of the team, we refer to a group.

A *group* will have members with different skills and abilities. They will be able to contribute these to a degree that will vary according to different circumstances. They will feel free to offer these skills and abilities to other group members and share their perceptions of what is happening in given circumstances.

Similarly, each member of a group will feel able to ask any other member of the group for help if it feels appropriate to do so. Thus, all roles within a group may be interchangeable. The degree to which this can be achieved will clearly depend upon the commitment of the group members. It will also depend to a large extent, of course, on the attitude of the nominated group leader.

If, for example, the group leader is overly conscious of her own status, it is unlikely she will be able to help her own group towards operating at its optimum. The more secure a group leader feels in her position the less she needs to express her status and the more effective the group is likely to become.

A team that is highly cohesive will operate as a group in the manner we have attempted to describe. It will share, not only in the abstract, but in very practical terms also.

A highly cohesive group will, within itself, offer and accept emotional support appropriately. It will share knowledge and perception, and moreover, actual tasks and workloads will be shared.

Members of a group will feel valued by other group members and will, in turn, value them.

All these aspects of group working inculcate feelings of well-being and increase confidence. This can only enhance the quality of client and patient contact.

A team that is, in contrast, low in cohesion, with members and leader unsure of themselves is likely to operate as a network. Each individual will work with a feeling of emotional isolation, needing to be reliant on her own resources only, without the support, commitment and strength of colleagues.

EXPECTATIONS

The expectations of an individual working within the different structures will vary according to how the structure is perceived.

In a hierarchy, the responsibility and the accountability of each individual are usually quite clearly defined.

Networks are not so clear. Indeed, networks are seldom described as networks. Organisations tend to see themselves as hierarchies or teams, or less frequently the group image may be projected. Despite a lack of overt recognition, networks are a very common working condition, where there is little clarity as to whom one can really call on for support.

The team may function as a set of individuals, answerable to themselves and the rules of their professional body. Alternatively, the structure may demand a responsibility and accountability to the team leader. Individuals may also be accountable to a professional superior outside the team.

Support is not always available as a matter of course, though such support may appear implicit.

When trying to decide which structure seems closest to her own working conditions, the reader may well become aware that the overt or stated structure in which she works may be very different from what she experiences. Often the stated, official and recognised structure has little relation to the reality.

We believe that this matters a great deal.

If, for example, we were working in what we recognised as a hierarchy we would turn to a superior for support, guidance or instructions. We would have quite a firm expectation that what is needed will be supplied. If what is needed is not forthcoming it is hardly surprising that feelings of frustration and insecurity are experienced. What has happened is that the hierarchy system has failed. It has, in effect, operated as a network.

Similarly, if we were working in what is called a team, we would be likely to have expectations of other team members. If these expectations are not met, then it is the team system that is failing. Again, we are likely to feel frustrated, let down and hurt and are therefore less likely to be able to work at our most effective level.

It will become clear that the authors consider it very important for everyone to identify for herself the system in which she works. If expectations are unrealistic, or are relevant to a different system from that in which you work, the result can not only be distressing but can lead to a degeneration of job satisfaction and a lessening of effective work.

It will also have become obvious that we believe appropriate support and supervision to be quite vital. Experience has shown that inadequate or inappropriate supervision and/or support has a direct effect upon performance, both professionally and personally. It can lead to the counsellor becoming stressed, tired and disillusioned, all of which have clear implications for the clients.

We believe that initially it is important to ask, if not demand, proper supervision from the agency for whom the counsellor works.

When adequate supervision is lacking it may well be that there are other issues in the agency that need addressing. These might include poor communication systems or an absence of effective in-service training. There may be little participation in decision making, boundaries may not be clear (or may be rigid and inflexible) and recognition and affirmation may be missing. To work effectively the counsellor has the right to such back-up and should have the confidence to ask for it.

However, in spite of the counsellor's best efforts this still may not be forthcoming. Others may be working in isolation.

There are, of course, many things that can be done to reduce stress. There may be a need to cut down on the work load — people under stress not infrequently compound the problem by undertaking still more work. Other stress-reducing techniques include the rewarding of oneself with 'treats' which could range from a long, relaxed bath to an exotic holiday — whatever feels like a treat to the individual concerned. Enjoyable exercise may be helpful, healthy physical fatigue helping to relax the mind. Relaxation techniques such as are described in Chapter Thirteen or meditation exercises are very valuable. Even if getting together with friends and laughing is the main stratagem used to relieve stress it is essential to make a conscious commitment for what is an essential activity.

None of this is a substitute for skilled supervision and it is incumbent on the counsellor to ensure that it is arranged. If supervision is not available within the agency or organisation then the counsellor needs to look elsewhere.

Possible sources for finding supervision are the British Association for Counselling, local colleges that offer courses in counselling, peer counselling or co-counselling with a colleague or another counsellor.

Whatever source you choose to find an appropriate counselling supervisor — don't leave home without one!

ACCOUNTABILITY AND CONFIDENTIALITY

The relevance for the purposes of clarity regarding the structure in which you are working is its direct effect on the relationship established in counselling. It is important that both counsellor and client are very clear as to where the counsellor sees her accountability to lie. It is equally important that confidentiality is not assumed by the client to be absolute when the counsellor feels committed to judge whether or not information received in counselling may be passed on.

The issues of accountability and confidentiality may be clearly defined by what the counsellor understands as her professional responsibility. It is more difficult where such responsibilities are not clearly defined.

It is absolutely vital that the client knows, before trusting a counsellor with personal confidences, how far the counsellor will regard such confidence as private.

These issues must be decided by each counsellor on an individual basis. It is easy to decide, perhaps, on major issues when important moral laws are violated and innocent people suffer, although even in such circumstances some counsellors feel that confidentially between client and counsellor must always be absolute.

It is less easy, and sometimes seems an intolerable decision to have to take, when a counsellor feels called upon to judge whether or not her knowledge should be used to alter a situation for what may appear to be the better.

Such a dilemma is not altogether unusual. An example concerns an 11-year-old girl. She was offered counselling by a worker in a professional agency, the referral problem being non-attendance at school and difficulty in relating to her peers.

During the fifth weekly session it emerged that the child and her stepfather indulged in a full sexual relationship. The child claimed that this did not distress her at all, on the contrary she said that since the onset of the relationship some three months previously, she felt that she had gained confidence. She asserted that her place in the family was more secure and she believed she was now happier with her friends. She was also now attending school regularly.

The counsellor knew that the child's mother was happy with her new husband, to whom she had been married for nearly a year. Her re-marriage had followed a particularly bitter divorce and several years of unhappy loneliness.

Clearly if the matter were reported to the statutory authorities, the family would be broken up and the new happiness and security of the mother and her children shattered. According to the child, her confidence would be diminished, her security lost and she would be left only with feelings of guilt.

If the counsellor did not inform anyone, the relationship between the child and her stepfather would probably continue. The alternative of offering counselling to the stepfather was not considered.

As a matter of interest, that particular counsellor decided to leave matters very much as they were. This occurred in the late 1970s. By 1983, the child had had one abortion, given birth to a child and was in a specialised psychiatric unit for adolescents. The stepfather was in prison, the mother was in a state of depression and the local authority were considering taking the younger child into care, though in the event this was not necessary.

It is, of course, a matter for speculation as to what would have happened should confidentiality have been breached or a different course of action have been decided.

This may be an extreme example, but the dilemma is the same in the less dramatic circumstances that most counsellors are likely to encounter.

Once a personal decision as to confidentiality has been reached, the position of the counsellor should be made quite clear to the client. Should, for example, a physiotherapist feel that she is obliged as a professional to report to her superior, or to the physician or surgeon, any information she receives that might affect a patient's progress, then she must make this clear to the patient/client. The client is then free to choose the extent to which such a counselling relationship can be used. Trust is established regarding limits, and trust is essential to any counselling relationship.

THE COUNSELLING CONTRACT

The clarification between client and counsellor regarding the issue of confidentiality forms part of the counselling contract. Once the potential counsellor has recognised and responded to a request from a potential client, it is important to clarify a number of points. Most of these have already been indicated but we will summarise the considerations that go to form a counselling contract.

1. The counsellor should state clearly the time that is available. The timing should be consistent, as far as possible, and adhered to.

When the client knows the time that the counselling session will end, he has the safety of knowing that any topics introduced at the end of the session cannot be explored immediately. He can then time his disclosures so that he is able to prepare himself for the possibly painful and difficult piece of work. The importance of this timing cannot be too strongly stressed. It is a major safety factor for the client. It is no coincidence that many inexperienced counsellors feel distress that a client 'only gets to the point' five minutes before the session is due to end.

Another possible reason for this last point may be a bid from the client for the counsellor's extended attention. In this case, a firm reminder of the time and a reassurance that the matter can be discussed at the next session may be appropriate.

2. The counsellor should state clearly the aims of the counselling. Unreal expectations can only be counter-productive. The client should be aware that he will be involved in 'work' towards achieving those aims.

3. The client should be helped to state his needs as he sees them at this time. It is not likely at the outset that he will be totally clear about them. However, the

arranging of the contract may take several sessions, and in any event the contract is not a fixed and final agreement as far as the client's needs are concerned.

4. The counsellor should make clear her position regarding confidentiality.

Should the counsellor feel it is appropriate to pass on information to a colleague or superior, or any other body including the police in extreme cases, the client should be made aware of this and of the reasons for such decisions. If it is then deemed necessary for information to be divulged it will not be a surprise or a betrayal to the client.

5. The client should make an undertaking regarding the confidentiality of any personal information the counsellor might disclose during sessions.

6. It is important that some form of notes or records be kept. At the very least certain facts that will remind the counsellor about important details regarding the client must be noted. Preferably, notes should also include significant details that have emerged during each session, which can provide a valuable record of the client's progress.

The client should, of course, be aware that such notes are being kept, and also that such records are for the counsellor alone.

7. The client should be made aware that his 'case' but not his identity will be discussed with his counsellor's supervisor.

Increasingly, clients of various agencies are being given access to their own files. This seems to be an issue that is likely to attract some public concern and which we should, as professionals, consider in an objective manner.

One of the major arguments for withholding the patient's (client's) file is that it may contain information that might in some way be harmful to him. In some instances, of course, this must be true. Often, though, we feel the 'harmful information' is more an example of the insensitivity of the writer than of a harmful fact. Some years ago a woman was described in a medical report as a 'manipulative lying hysteric'. When this lady's daughter was 18 she requested that she see the file. The above quotation regarding her mother had been used in virtually every report that had been compiled over a great many years. Investigation of later events showed that the quotation was not only grossly insensitive, it was also inaccurate.

If the possibility that our clients may see their records prompts us to think more carefully and to write more sensitively then the move towards access to files can be no bad thing. It is a different matter if this move should prevent accurate recording, or inhibit the keeping of full records.

Perhaps the guideline should be that a sensitive counsellor will have been congruent with her client, and nothing in the file would come as a shock should the client read it.

The counselling contract is usually verbal, though there is no reason why it should not be written if this seems appropriate, and it may take some time to formalise. During the course of a counselling relationship the contract regarding the specific aims for the client may be altered or restated. We suggest that this should be done in a relatively formal manner to ensure clarity for both the client and counsellor.

The construction of a contract may seem forbidding or formal. In practice, it offers the client safe boundaries and is helpful in focusing the client's attention and energy.

The contract also identifies counselling as a professional skill with its own values and disciplines, which in itself may give the client more confidence.

In addition, the contract helps to establish trust and gives the counsellor a guideline with each client. Trust must, obviously, be an important component of every counselling relationship. Formulating a contract along the lines we have suggested can offer security to a person in an insecure position. It gives a framework within which the client can feel safe to express feelings which the counsellor feels confident to receive.

8.

COUNSELLING A PERSON WITH SPEECH DIFFICULTIES AND LANGUAGE IMPAIRMENT

A two-way communications system, for example, two people in a telephone conversation, would be represented by a communication engineer as Figure 8.1.

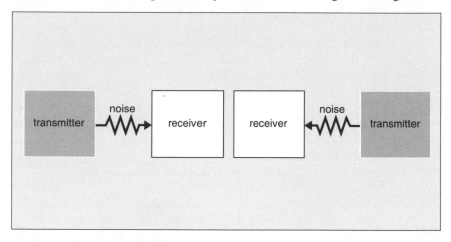

Fig. 8.1 A two-way communication system.

The quality of signal received in both cases is degraded by the unavoidable introduction of noise. The noise is either generated internally by the system, or externally by background noises.

If we apply this description to the counselling situation, the communication is that between counsellor and client. The noise is any interference that distorts or interrupts that communication. Noise generated within the system, the system in this case being the counsellor or the client, can be defined as any blocks, defences or fears that prevent the client from stating clearly what he wishes to communicate, or the counsellor from hearing or understanding with clarity.

Noise defined as background noise can represent any other factors hampering communication.

The client with speech and communication difficulties is, of course, only one small problem among many. The reader may well wonder why this client should be represented in apparent preference to any other.

This client has needs that are no different to those of any of us, but the number of people available to him may be very limited. Someone with speech that is difficult to understand, or who uses an alternative means of communication, does have special difficulties. He often has difficulty in establishing himself as an adult person.

In the majority of encounters he has to overcome other people's embarrassment and lack of understanding. Many of the people he encounters assume that his needs are only practical. Many will be unwilling to admit that they have not understood what he is saying to them and will mumble meaningless reassurance or jump to erroneous conclusions without checking that they are correct. Many clients with severe communication difficulties have said that even those knowing them well always assume initially that any request is for the lavatory.

It is therefore likely that a member of the paramedical professions who will be assumed to be familiar with cerebral palsy or stroke, for example, will be asked for counselling by someone with communication problems.

In this situation, the art of listening is particularly important.

It is essential to be honest, and never pretend understanding when you are not sure what you have heard. Anyone would rather repeat even several times what they have said than have doubts about whether they have been understood.

Should you be unable to comprehend even after several attempts it may be helpful to ask the client if he can use different words. Spelling, or giving the initial letter of problem words can help. Do not assume that this will be possible. Many people with speech difficulties will have perceptual problems that can make spelling or sound recognition impossible, but to ask if the client is able to spell the word will establish to the sensitive listener whether or not this is possible.

Should all these possibilities fail then the technique of 'arrow' questioning can help. This involves a gradual narrowing down of the possibilities by asking questions that can be answered with 'yes' or 'no.'

First establish with the client, should there be any doubt, how these yes and no answers are conveyed. The words may be used clearly, or a nod and shake of the head used. Other signs may be used by clients unable to use head gestures clearly. These can be established by saying to the client, 'Will you show me how you say yes?' When you are clear about this, then ask, 'How do you say no?' As a practical measure it may be helpful to make a note of any signals that are idiosyncratic to the client. It may be very clear that a client looks up for yes and down for no, but it is all too easy to forget which is which in the course of discussion.

Questions requiring either a positive or a negative response can then be asked.

In the following example, the adolescent cerebral palsied boy (L) concerned signalled yes, no and don't know by hand movements. He had at that time no alternative means of communication.

He was very distressed and had communicated that he wished to talk to the counsellor (C) in school.

C. Is it something to do with school?
L. Yes. No. Yes. No.
C. To do with school and somewhere else?
L. Yes.
C. Hospital?
L. No.
C. Home?
L. Yes.
C. Something at home is affecting school?

L. No.
C. Something at school that is affecting home?
L. Yes.
C. So there is something going on at school that is causing problems at home?
L. Yes.
C. Right. Is it to do with you specifically?
L. Yes.
C. Is it something you want me to talk to your parents about?
L. NO. NO. NO. NO.
C. OK, I hear you. Is it something they don't know about?
L. Yes.
C. Is it something I know about?
L. Yes.
C. Something in class?
L. Yes.
C. Is it something in class this week?
L. Yes.
C. Right. Tell me when I get to it. I will go through the lessons and you stop me when I get there. OK?
L. Yes.
C. Swimming? Physio? Reading? Speech? Singing? School Leavers' Programme?
L. Yes.
C. The School Leavers' Programme. A particular thing?
L. No.
C. Just generally about leaving?
L. Yes.
C. About leaving school?
L. Yes.
C. Luke, is it OK if I make a guess?
L. Yes.
C. Is it that there are difficulties with your parents in talking about your leaving school?
L. Yes. [At this point Luke became very distressed]
C. OK, so we've got there. Shall we take this a bit further?
L. Yes.
C. OK, but you tell me 'No' if you want me to stop. Will you do that?
L. Yes.
C. Do you want to talk to your parents about leaving school?
L. Yes.
C. Have you any ideas about why they won't talk to you?
L. Yes.
C. Do you want to tell me what you think about that?
L. Yes.
C. I may make some pretty daft guesses. Can you cope with that?
L. Yes. [Laughing]

C. OK. Good for you. Do you think it is because they are waiting to talk to the Careers Officer?

L. No.

C. To be asked to come up to the school?

L. No.

C. Is it that they don't want to think about it?

L. Yes. [Looking a question]

C. I'm on the right track? [pause] Luke, do you want to leave home when you grow up?

L. Yes. Yes. Yes. [very agitated]

C. Do you think your parents will allow you to do so?

L. No. No. No.

C. Will you have any choice?

L. No. [Begins to sob]

C. OK, love, we're beginning to get there and it hurts. Can you stay with it for a while?

L. Yes.

C. Let's check out again. They won't talk about when you leave school because as far as they are concerned you will be living at home with them. Will you be doing anything, do you think?

L. No.

C. That must feel pretty desperate. I wonder how you feel? Pretty put-down, I should guess?

L. Yes.

C. Do you have any idea what you want to do, given the chance?

L. Don't know.

C. Would it help if you did? If we talked about it?

L. Yes.

C. Well, we shall be talking about your various possibilities in class. Do you want to do anything about your parents at this moment?

L. No.

C. Do you want me to do anything about them?

L. No.

C. That seems a wise decision to me. Shall we talk about it again when you know a bit more and have listened to the other kids and what their ideas are?

L. Yes.

C. Is there anything more? Do you want to talk some more?

L. No.

It will be noticed that all the questions demanded either a yes or no. This may seem too obvious to worth stating, but it is surprising how many people will ask an either/or question which is impossible to answer in such circumstances.

An occasional summary of the facts is helpful, and any mistakes can be identified quickly. It is also important to state clearly when the counsellor is hazarding a guess, and to make it clear that a rejection of that guess is not only acceptable but likely. It is rare for a client to agree with an incorrect assumption in a misguided attempt to please the counsellor but it can happen.

The process may seem laborious and frustrating, but it must be remembered that there are usually very few opportunities for such a severely disabled person to talk about his feelings. If the counsellor is able to relax and does not allow her anxieties to block her ability to communicate much will be gained.

It is important that the counsellor is able to concentrate fully on what the client is saying. With difficult speech, any background noise, conflicting demands on the counsellor's attention, or the presence of another person who insists on giving interpretations, all make it unlikely that understanding will be achieved.

If the counsellor is unfamiliar with the client it can be very helpful for someone who is familiar with him to be present initially. In these circumstances 'neutral' topics should be discussed until the counsellor feels able to communicate with the client in a confidential setting and with a confident manner. Very few counsellors would consider counselling a client with a third party present (unless the counselling was with a couple and that was the contract). The severely disabled client should not be treated any differently in this respect.

Any additional aids to communication can be useful when speech proves inadequate. The young man in the next transcript preferred to use speech but relied upon a POSSUM communicator, spelling and gesture when the counsellor could not understand.

There are a number of artificial aids to communication that may be used to supplement or replace speech. The POSSUM communicator incorporates a display board arranged in a similar order to a typewriter keyboard. A light traverses the letters on the display and is controlled by the user with a switch — in Jon's case operated by one foot. When the desired letter is indicated by the light the switch is operated to print out and the light recommences its traverse. A far less laborious method is now available using a microcomputer, which can be operated using switches adapted to the physical ability of the user. The word-store function of the computer can make its use much quicker than the individual letter-by-letter method of the POSSUM.

Jon was able to use his POSSUM effectively despite his poor spelling ability. (J = Jon, C = Counsellor.)

J.   [Three attempts at a sentence]
C.   I'm still not getting it. What is it about?
J.   Me.
C.   OK. Sentence starts, 'I'?
J.   AM.
C.   I am. Yes?
J.   I am going.
C.   Where are you going?
J.   [Several unintelligible attempts]
C.   The name of a place?
J.   Yes. [Using POSSUM] — a home.
C.   You are going to a home. A residential home?
J.   Yes. I feel terrible. I don't want to go.
C.   That is really making you feel bad.
J.   I know I've got to go. Mum [Unintelligible]
C.   Something about Mum?

J. [Indicates his own back]
C. Mum had a bad back?
J. She can't manage me. I'm too big.
C. But you don't feel so big when it comes to leaving her.
J. I feel really awful.
C. Jon, terrible and awful are really vivid words. Can you identify these feelings more clearly still?
J. [After some thought] I feel terrible about leaving Mum.
C. Yes, but it's that same word again.
J. I want to cry.
C. You feel very sad about leaving Mum?
J. Yes. And sad.
C. Sad and sad?
J. [Apparently repeating 'sad']
C. Sorry, I'm still hearing 'sad'.
J. [Very loudly] M-A-D. [Saying the letters]
C. MAD! You feel mad. You are angry — good and angry?
J. [Stamping and shouting] Yes, yes, yes.
C. Who are you mad with, Jon?
J. [Thoughtfully] Not Mum.
C. Not with Mum. Who, then?
J. [Turning to POSSUM] I do not no.
C. I don't feel as if I believe that.
J. Why?
C. Well, partly because you let the POSSUM say it for you, and partly because I'm feeling anxious in myself.
J. I don't know who.
C. I hear you say you don't know who you are mad with. Right. [A long pause]
J. I thought — I thought — you [Unintelligible]
C. What did you think about me?
J. I thought you would [Unintelligible]
C. Sorry, I still can't get it.
J. S-T-O-P.
C. Stop? You thought I would stop it happening? Wow! That feels like real power. I'm surprised you dare feel mad with me.
J. Not really.
C. Not really what? Mad, or believing I could stop you having to go into a home?
J. I didn't think you could really stop it.
C. Aha! But you are mad with me?
J. Yes.
C. Can you tell me why you are mad with me?
J. Not you.
C. You can't tell me?
J. No. Not you going.
C. I don't have to go into a home?
J. Yes.

In this extract from a counselling session Jon did not always use speech successfully, but made quite certain he was understood.

The incident where Jon used POSSUM rather than speech demonstrates that even in clients with difficult speech, choice of words can convey more than their immediate meaning. The counsellor was aware of uneasy feelings, noticed the use of POSSUM and shared her impressions with the client. When he repeated his assertion she reflected back to him. She then allowed a silence, which gave Jon the chance to consider whether he dared to say how he really felt — which he wanted to do and which he managed to do.

Congruence, reflection, non-possessive warmth and confrontation are all demonstrated in this extract and the young man was able to begin to identify the feelings he was experiencing.

OTHER COMMUNICATION DIFFICULTIES

Some speech difficulties, notably those following some strokes, some conditions of congenital brain damage and in severe traumatic brain damage, present a much more difficult problem.

The client may be fully aware of what he wishes to say but the words he produces may not make sense (as in the early stage of some right hemiplegias). If the client is aware of this and can indicate 'yes' and 'no' reliably, it may be possible to use arrow questions. It is important to reassure the client that you know he has something to say but is being prevented from using speech.

Sometimes the client is unaware that his speech is unintelligible. He will become extremely bewildered and angry at what he sees as people's refusal to listen to him. In these cases even the yes/no response may be unreliable and it is not always possible to be sure that speech is understood. However, many who have progressed beyond this stage have clear memories of understanding everyone else and being terrified and humiliated at their own inability to communicate.

An explanation to the client of what is happening, a warm and reassuring manner with the use of touch to reinforce your speech and an acknowledgement of how distressing the inability to communicate must be, may be all the counsellor is able to offer. However, warmth, sympathy and understanding expressed unequivocally to another human being can be a healing contrast to the unrelenting jollity or patronising delegation to infant status so often experienced by those deprived of the means to communicate with speech.

It is important to make a clear statement here. It is always preferable to assume that anyone you may contact is an intelligent, sensitive and feeling fellow human, and to speak to him or her accordingly. You will more often than not be correct in your assumption and to be wrong does no harm.

Anyone involved in counselling in disability or illness could tell of numerous instances when highly intelligent and aware people were treated as less than human by fellow humans whose intelligence has failed to see beyond their outward appearance. The training of these professional people does not seem to have enlightened them in this area.

Having made this statement, one must then say that there appear to be some conditions when the client may not make sense and when he seems unaware that he is not communicating.

The petit mal form of epilepsy can so fragment a person's continuity of experience and communication that the world he inhabits can be bewilderingly different from that the counsellor experiences. An example from the classroom of a school for children with disability may explain this more clearly.

A teacher was explaining to a group of children how the first stage of making a calender was to be achieved. She told the children, 'Choose a picture from the box. Cut very carefully round the picture so that you have the part you want. Then choose a piece of card the shape you want — there are circles and squares. Glue the picture on to the card carefully. Don't cut the card, choose one of the shapes, a circle or a square.'

The children set to work. As all the children were disabled, many needed considerable help and Bill, being reasonably dextrous, was left to get on with the task on his own.

When the teacher reached him she was annoyed to find that he had glued the picture on to a square of card and then cut both card and picture into an uneven circle. Both picture and card were wasted.

The teacher told Bill he must listen and remember what he was told. Bill said indignantly that he had listened and had done as the teacher instructed. The teacher became angry at the silly excuse and Bill became sulky and refused to make any more effort.

This incident could very easily be interpreted as Bill's not attending and then trying to defend his fault, but Bill suffered from frequent attacks of petit mal. These fits, not obvious to the observer, resulted in short periods of loss of consciousness. What Bill may have heard the teacher say was something like, 'Cut . . . the picture . . . you want . . . piece of card . . . glue . . . cut the card . . . circle.'

Although the teacher was aware that Bill suffered from petit mal, she had never had explained to her the effect this would have on his perception of the world and on his comprehension of language. This is not altogether surprising. Teachers of children with special needs do not have medical training and will often be expected to teach children with a wide range of physical, emotional, educational and psychological needs.

Because of the continuous nature of petit mal attacks Bill would not be aware that he was hearing the teacher's words any differently from any other child. He has always existed in a world fragmented in this way. He would, as usual, make the best sense of what he heard. His actions are then explained and his anger, bewilderment and hurt understandable.

When communicating with a client suffering from petit mal it may be sufficient to repeat key phrases — for example, 'How are you feeling today? Are you feeling alright? How are you today?'

Similarly, if the client's response is fragmented, ask him to repeat his statement or reflect back to him what you think you heard.

This might make communication seem laborious and unnatural but can be the best way of achieving an understanding. It is certainly preferable to employing the sort of loud, slow and carefully articulated speech that is commonly employed by so many people when speaking to foreigners and the mentally disabled!

A severely epileptic person having very frequent attacks of petit mal may have so much of his everyday experience distorted and fragmented that his attitude may appear very disturbed and counselling impossible.

In these circumstances perhaps all the counsellor can do is to respond with warmth and acceptance to the client. It may be possible to reinforce those experiences that seem to relate to the 'real world' with warmth and encouragement, and to accept without comment, but with positive sympathy, the negative statements that do not appear to be rooted in reality.

In some forms of brain damage, notably in that resulting in the 'cocktail party syndrome' seen in some clients with spina bifida and hydrocephalus, words seem to be in a different currency to that usually accepted.

In the cocktail party syndrome, the client will talk fluently and frequently with a sophisticated and extensive vocabulary. When this occurs in young children or adolescents an impression of startling intelligence can be conveyed. To the listener, after a time a sense of bewilderment ensues. The listener seems to lose the thread of the discourse, to miss vital connecting points. Phrases seem to recur with a parrot-like facility. The words and expressions used do not seem to be relevant to the apparent subject under discussion and even the subject changes suddenly and without reason. The whole conversation seems to bear less and less relation to the apparent ability and intelligence of the speaker.

A child will learn very early in life behaviour that attracts attention and gains approval. The curious precocity of speech apparent in these cocktail party syndrome children attracts a great deal of adult comment and approval and the initial symptom is reinforced into a behaviour pattern.

Sadly, as a child gets older, remarks which are startling and thus amusing to adults when made by a two- or three-year-old are less appealing in an eight-year-old. The child usually has great difficulty in understanding how to establish realistic relationships in any case, and will cling to the formula which was successful in the past. The child does not understand what appears to be a withdrawal of approval and becomes unhappy and resentful.

For example, a very pretty and appealing little girl of three used to attract a great deal of attention when she wagged an admonitory finger at an adult and said roguishly, 'Don't you tell me what to do, you impertinent fellow.'

When she was nine and still responding to adult instruction with the same and similar phrases, teachers and therapists not unnaturally became irritated. The child was totally unable to understand the inappropriateness of her behaviour and became very angry at the adults' rejection of her.

When it was attempted to explain to her that her words were rude, her response was, 'You are rude', and when she was told that she must in some circumstances do as she was told, she parroted, 'You do as you are told.'

Such children can grow up isolated from their peers and be the source of frustration and irritation to adults.

Children do not relate easily to a peer who talks to them like a pedantic and disapproving adult. A thirteen-year-old girl explained to one of the authors in front of her class-mates, 'These children display a lamentable ignorance of the correct way to treat me. They do not accord me proper respect or do as I tell them.'

Such children can seem unable to reason, relate cause and effect, or make logical connections. Things learned in one context are not related to another context. For example, independence skills learned in one environment seem to be totally forgotten when their use is expected in a similar situation elsewhere.

To attempt to counsel such a client, either as child or adult, can be a discouraging experience. Seemingly important statements can, when explored, seem to change, disappear or become increasingly convoluted and obscure. The apparent subject will be changed abruptly and bewilderingly. The stated problems or experiences will contradict previously established facts.

Yet frequently such clients are lonely, unhappy and discontented, with frequent outbursts of aggression and no close relationships. They tend to approach every contact and agency with a long list of problems and complaints. They are people obviously in need of help.

The authors have found that in such circumstances client-centred therapy, as we have described it, is not useful. The client may well enter such a relationship with enormous enthusiasm and eagerly relate story after story of their childhood, relationships, disability and its related experiences but no movement is made and the counsellor can feel herself becoming more and more deeply enmeshed in a sterile relationship that becomes increasingly more difficult to envisage ending.

We do not know the answer to this dilemma. Attempts at some modification of inappropriate behaviour by positive suggestion and reinforcement by praise may sometimes help but the long-term outcome is of dubious value.

Experience would suggest that a positive and encouraging reinforcement of acceptable behaviour patterns, when these occur, can help. The suggestion of clear strategies for dealing with difficulties, when these can be identified, with a strongly expressed approval of success may modify behaviour to a limited degree.

The counsellor does run the risk of her counsel being parroted abroad, of course, and applied dogmatically in inappropriate circumstances. The client may become so strongly attracted to the counselling relationship with its reward of undivided attention and approval of another person, that his demands may become overwhelming. In such circumstances we suggest a firm, kind and matter-of-fact refusal to offer the time needed for relating a long catalogue of grievances. This, together with the strongly positive suggestion that a client is someone for whom the counsellor has a warm and positive regard, may well be all that can realistically be offered.

There are clients able to use speech whose communication still poses problems for the counsellor.

Some medical conditions result in toneless, monotonous speech. This may be accompanied by correspondingly expressionless features. Examples that come to mind are Parkinson's disease and ataxic cerebral palsy.

Expressive speech may not always correspond to the feelings of the client. Apparently casual and light speech mannerisms may mask deep feelings — again, this can happen with ataxia. In athetosis, paradoxical expression may occur when the client will laugh or cry in total opposition to how he is feeling.

In these circumstances, the counsellor needs to be very aware of and sensitive to all the clues available to her — body language may help (although this is often equally unreliable in these conditions). Reflecting the words used and accompanying them with a query about the possible surrounding feelings is useful.

For example, a young man with ataxic cerebral palsy said, 'My girl friend is leaving the Home to go to another one next month. She has got a transfer.' His face was without any expression except faint boredom and his voice was casual and off-hand.

The counsellor responded, 'The girl you are fond of is going away. I would feel — I don't know. Sad? Angry? I wonder how you feel about that?'

The response was, 'I don't know why she did that without saying anything to me. We were going to get engaged. She never talked to me about wanting to go away.'

His deep hurt and sense of betrayal he talked about, but no alteration in his expression or in the tone of his voice was apparent.

Stammering may also be associated with illness or disability, as may similar speech disabilities that block fluent speech. In these cases, the counsellor's main function is to offer time, a relaxed atmosphere and freedom from her own anxieties. Clients who stammer are not helped by well-meaning offers of possible interpretation of what they are attempting to say, or by being instructed to 'Relax, take your time.' A receptive, warm but relaxed and undemanding listener is the best facilitator.

NON-VERBAL COMMUNICATION

When no speech is possible, due to congenital defect, brain damage following trauma or progressive neuromuscular disorders, alternative means of communication may be used. These vary from a simple picture-board on which a patient can indicate basic needs, to symbol systems such as Blissymbolics, manual signing languages or synthetic speech.

To deal briefly with synthetic speech, it needs to be said that some synthetic speech is still of a robot-like quality. Initially, the counsellor needs to become familiar with the sound of the speech. When she can understand what is being said, the suggestions we have already made regarding monotonous speech apply. In addition, the counsellor should be very careful to talk to the client — not to the apparatus from which the speech comes. This is obvious but is an insidious trap, and it is all too easy to find oneself answering the machine and not looking at the client whose speech the machine is supplying.

When counselling clients who use other alternatives to speech the counsellor should, whenever possible, work initially with someone who understands the system used by the client. These initial interviews should, as when working with clients with difficult speech, be of a general nature until the counsellor feels able to be alone with the client in a confidential setting. The guide-lines given at the beginning of this chapter are, of course, applicable to clients using alternative means of communication.

In the authors' experience the greatest barrier to communication with the client using signing or symbol language is the anxiety of the counsellor. She feels that her inability to understand is a reflection of her own value. She 'ought' to be able to comprehend, and a failure to do so is difficult to accept.

Anxiety often blocks a counsellor's ability to begin to work easily in an unfamiliar mode. Her anxiety may communicate to the client and may block his ability to use his system effectively. This is especially true of, for example, a severely disabled client with athetosis using eye-pointing with Blissymbolics.

The other barrier is that of not allowing sufficient time. To convey a message may take a long time and several repetitions. Usually the counsellor is more aware of this time than the client. Where a symbol or signing system has always been the only way a client has been able to communicate he will be used to the length of time this takes. The alternative is, after all, the tedious and unsatisfactory one of yes/no interrogation.

For those whom trauma or illness has robbed of speech, inability to understand on the part of the counsellor may be more frustrating. Congruence usually helps. To share feelings of inadequacy and impotence with the client together with a request for patience on his part seldom fails. To acknowledge and accept the client's anger at the counsellor's incompetence can defuse a difficult situation. With these feelings acknowledged, the way is open to mutual sharing of communication.

Signing may be used by deaf clients or by those who have a physical or neurological barrier to speech but whose manual dexterity is sufficiently good to make signs feasible.

British Sign Language, Makaton and Amer-Ind are systems where hand gestures stand for words. Paget-Gorman uses very precise gestures to represent words, tenses and parts of speech on a highly sophisticated level. Finger spelling is sometimes used alone or may reinforce or supplement other signs.

Apart from finger spelling, which is relatively easily learned, it may be necessary always to work through an interpreter. This interpreter should, whenever possible, be someone entirely neutral and, of course, someone who understands and pledges total confidentiality. This interpreter will be included in the counselling contract.

Symbol systems are designed to be used by anyone, and are either self-explanatory or, as in the case of Blissymbolics, the relevant word is printed above the symbol in the user's chart or book. Clients may use a symbol system in a direct or simple way. A client using Blissymbols indicated the symbols for I, feel, angry, Grandad, say, I, baby. (Symbols may not be indicated in syntactical order. Users often seem to express their internal language in order of importance of the words in their thoughts. Such a message may be indicated in the order angry, I, baby, Grandad, say, I.)

Most users prefer the listener to say each word as it is indicated so that he is sure the correct symbol has been perceived. When the whole message is complete (and we would advise writing the symbol words down) the reader will then reflect what she interprets as the meaning to the client.

Should the meaning not be immediately clear, arrow questions can be used to clarify or the client asked to repeat or re-form the message.

An experienced and skilled user will employ metaphor and form colloquialisms to develop his own individual and personally idiosyncratic 'speech'. He can use combinations of symbols to create new words or meanings and is able to express himself with great clarity and flexibility.

A relatively complex Bliss communication is demonstrated in the ideas below, communicated by a young boy in a discussion. We give the message exactly as it was communicated and then present it in 'normal speech'.

I, past tense, to hear, plural, person, think, when, you, die, you, come, on, earth, in, new, person. I, like, the, idea. I, future tense, to come, future, time, no, handicap. I, think, many, plural, person, need, to hear, what, I, past tense, hear, because, to be, handicap, not, sad, when, you, know, combined symbol, life, come, more, close combine.

(I heard people think when you die you come down on earth in a new person. I like the idea. I will come next time with no handicap. I think many people need to hear what I heard because to be handicapped is not sad when you know about reincarnation.)

When a client has learning difficulties his understanding of language and his use of language may be delayed to a greater or lesser degree. This may range from an inability to understand complex ideas or vocabulary to a level where spoken language is neither understood or used. At the lowest level, pictures may be meaningless, other's expressions not understood and the only communication with other people that may be recognised is touch. In the last case counselling in any form will not be appropriate.

There may be specific areas of language delay: a client may be unable to understand abstract ideas, or be unable to recognise past or future, for example.

It is important to assess the nature of the difficulty.

For example, Sarah, an adult with global learning difficulties, was unable to understand money, tell the time or relate to the passage of time. Her speech was clear but consisted largely of sets of cliches and 'wise sayings' associated with particular circumstances. Her attention span was very limited and she quickly tired of any subject. Attempts to recapture her attention when she had lost interest made her angry.

However, she was obviously confused, distressed and frightened about an incident that had occurred involving an indecent assault upon her.

It was clear to the counsellor that Sarah had difficulty in finding the language to express her feelings about what had happened to her. The counsellor was able to draw with some facility and Sarah was enthusiastic. After drawing some pictures to Sarah's instructions the counsellor said 'How could I draw the man who hurt you?'

Susan said, 'A big, black door in my head. Bad things behind the door.' Using this striking image, the counsellor with Sarah made a door in the centre of a sheet of card and coloured it black. The counsellor drew and coloured 'good things' on one side, following Sarah's instructions. Then Sarah herself said, 'Open the door. Draw bad things.'

Sarah then gave clear instructions to the counsellor which disclosed not only the details of the recent abuse but of past incidents. This process continued over a number of weeks. After each picture was completed on the 'bad' side Sarah reassured herself by closing the door over it and saying, 'all shut away.'

Sarah continued this very vivid use of imagery, eventually asking for the 'bad' side of the picture to be cut away. She then had to decide what to do with it. She considered several options, talking seriously.

'Draw big flowers on it. No. Still there. Put it in bin. No, not rubbish.' Then she smiled broadly and handed it to the counsellor.

'You look after it.'

Sarah's ability to use imagery (at a later date she described her position as 'me and the Centre, me and the Home, backwards and forwards, bat and ball, I'm the ball') is not unusual in people whose verbal abilities may be limited. A child with no language beyond a few single words and with severe physical disability used small dolls to represent her family. After naming each doll ('Me, Mummy, Daddy, Nanny, Wayne) she arranged them with herself and her mother centrally, Nanny and Daddy isolated at a distance and her brother Wayne far away with his back turned. She wasn't satisfied and demanded sticky tape. She then bound the doll representing herself firmly to the mother's back. When she replaced the dolls the mother doll fell over. She looked up and said in a very strong voice. 'too much. On 'er back. Me.' She then swept all the dolls away, apparently very satisfied at what she had told.

Other ways of using symbolic activities are described in Chapter Thirteen and, although many of these are valuable when working with any client, some are of particular value when working with clients who have learning difficulties.

When language, however simple, is understood the counsellor will need to be very sensitive in balancing the need to use simple and clear language, to repeat herself and clarify what she has understood the client to say, with the over-riding need to convey respect for the client and for his right to choose and be in control. Many clients with learning difficulties have been brought up to obey adults and to conform to a rigid set of standards. The counsellor should not criticise the client for following imposed forms of behaviour (or for breaking them) or put pressure on the client to behave in a particular way. The client may need information, for example, as to the possible results of a particular course of action. It is not the counsellor's role to then forbid or encourage the action, but to encourage the client to explore what he sees as the areas for decision.

The counsellor may sometimes find herself in the position of being expected to implement decisions of social services or the directors of residential homes — or even parents — in her work with a client. She should make it very clear what her role is, both to these authorities and to the client, before starting work with a client with learning difficulties.

Whatever means a client may use to communicate his needs and feelings, the counselling skills employed are the same as those used when working with clients who are able to express themselves without difficulty. The need may often be greater. The counselling availability may be far more difficult for the client to find.

The rewards for the counsellor working in this field are correspondingly great.

NOTE

For those readers who are interested in alternative communication methods, the following addresses may be useful:

The Co-ordinating Group for Communication Systems
c/o The Wolfson Centre, Mecklenburgh Square, London WC1N 2AP

Amer-Ind
7 Chester Close, Lichfield WS13 7SX

Blissymbolics
Blissymbolics Communication Resource Centre
The South Glamorgan Institute of Higher Education
Western Avenue, Llandaff, Cardiff CF5 2YB

British Sign Language
The Royal National Institute for the Deaf
105 Gower Street, London WC1E 6AH

Cued Speech
The National Centre for Cued Speech
66–68 Upper Richmond Road
London SW15 2RP

Makaton Vocabulary
The Makaton Vocabulary Development Project
31 Forwood Drive, Camberley, Surrey GU15 3QD

Paget-Gorman Sign System
106 Morell Avenue, Oxford OX4 1NA

9.

SEXUALITY

ESTABLISHING SEXUAL IDENTITY

In almost every race, culture, religion and class children become aware very early in their lives of the sex to which they belong and of the expectations of that sex imposed by the society in which they live. As well as learning the political or social demands, children develop an awareness of physical and physiological differences between the sexes. The majority of children usually relate to their biological gender and will develop their own sexual identity.

For some children this process is not so simple. Their sense of gender may conflict with their biological identity. They may receive confusing messages about sexual roles from adults close to them. They may reject gender linked expectations or feel forced to emulate role models against their natural feelings.

For children who are disabled there can be additional problems.

In a society where masculinity is equated with physical strength and competence a boy who is disabled may feel that achieving male status is an impossibility. Other stereotyped masculine attributes — to be the principal wage earner, the responsible adult caring for his family's material needs, the protector — may seem unattainable aims. In adolescence a boy unable to experience erections or with delayed development of secondary sexual characteristics may despair of ever growing up to manhood.

Similarly, a girl may feel that she can only be a woman if she is physically attractive to men, or if she marries and has children. When she becomes aware that this may pose what seems to be insurmountable problems her sexual identity is threatened.

Disability may also involve physical caring by others. An essential part of normal sexual development is the establishment of a body image. A child who has happily run around naked will suddenly develop a frequently exaggerated 'modesty' even within a family where to be seen unclothed is the norm. The child is learning to define which areas of his body are intimate and to identify himself as a sexual being. He is establishing personal barriers, separating himself in a physical as well as an emotional sense from other people. He is becoming a clearly defined individual.

A child who does not have the opportunity to choose who may see or touch his body, who has to accept intimate handling, who is too often denied even minimal privacy is deprived of this process.

It is frightening how often the need for physical respect can be not just forgotten but not even recognised. A boy of fifteen, severely physically disabled and non-verbal following brain injury, was reported as being very distressed while his hips were being x-rayed. The therapist accompanying him felt he had been afraid of the x-ray machine.

When the boy was allowed to communicate his feelings about the episode he reported that he had been stripped naked and placed on the table in the presence of the therapist, the young female radiographer and five medical students, two of whom were female. He felt angry and humiliated — even more so when those present tried to reassure him that the machine wouldn't hurt him and he needn't be frightened!

The therapist found it hard to believe that the explanation of the boy's distress was true until the counsellor asked her if her own fifteen-year-old son would feel happy being stripped naked in front of such an audience and then made to lie in full view on a table. She was then appropriately horrified and contrite.

This may be (we hope) an extreme example, but it may be salutary for all our readers to consider carefully if they are always sensitive to the need for privacy and respect of *all* their patients.

ACQUIRED DISABILITY AND SEXUAL IDENTITY

Ben felt emasculated and humiliated by the physical limitations of his disability. He felt impotent; and literal impotence was also his experience. He no longer felt a man, the bread winner, the strong parent and carer. He had been deprived of his sexual identity.

Even when there is no directly physical cause of impotence, inability to obtain erections is a common experience for men who feel less than masculine because of acquired disability. Impotence is very often perceived as failure, and this additional failure compounds the problem.

Women who become disabled may feel unattractive or even repulsive. Limitation of movement or pain, deformity, the mutilation of surgery can all attack a woman's self image to a destructive degree. When a woman's sexual identity depends on feeling physically desirable disability may negate her feelings of femininity.

ATTITUDES

In many schools, sex education either forms part of the science curriculum and consists of a biological account of copulation and reproduction, or it is completely ignored. In many groups of teenagers, young people are found to have had either no sex education at all or have gleaned their knowledge from the media, their equally uninformed peers or observation.

In many Special Needs Schools the situation is even worse. The classroom teaching time is often in conflict with needs for therapy and physical care and priorities are seen as literacy and numeracy. Teachers feel that sex education is a specialist responsibility and should be given by the medical staff; school nurses are overstretched already and 'formal' sex education is not part of their remit. There is a feeling among some professionals, as well as the less informed public, that sexuality and its expression is not relevant to people who are disabled. Adults may be unable to face what they perceive as the destruction of hopes of a 'normal' adult life for a child who is disabled.

An often heard statement is 'We will always answer a child's questions'. Even assuming a child knows what to ask, and is able to find an appropriate person to ask, how often, we wonder, is such a question answered adequately — or accurately?

The absence of adequate sex education implies that information about contraception, genetic counselling and the avoidance of sexually transmitted diseases has been equally neglected.

For the adult with an acquired disability the possibilities for help can be equally bleak.

Many patients are given no information about the implications of their disability relevant to their sexual relationships. They may feel too fearful or embarrassed to ask.

Information can be callously incorrect (spinally injured people told that 'your sex life is over' for example) or woefully unimaginative (is a sexual relationship really only expressed by penetrative intercourse?).

The possibility of a patient needing such information can be contemptuously dismissed. We have heard of a man of sixty with Parkinson's disease being told that he shouldn't need to think about sex at his age; a young woman was asked why she wanted to know, she wasn't married after all?

THE COUNSELLOR'S ROLE

For the same reasons that you may be asked for help with other problems, you may be asked for help with problems involving sexuality and its expression.

It is therefore important to be prepared for such a request.

It is essential to be informed. Many of us will have received inadequate sex education, some may have a hazy idea of genital anatomy or the range and variety of sexual expression. We may find this area more difficult than any other to be non-judgemental and accepting of other people's sexual practices. Our personal opinions may range from feeling that sexual intercourse in any other way than the 'missionary position' is perverted, to a belief that anything that gives the participants pleasure and hurts no-one is acceptable. (Anyone tending towards the first should consider the situation of a woman with brittle bones or one partner with contracted hip joints). It may be difficult to accept that people who are disabled may be gay or lesbian, or to accept a man with learning difficulties who is transvestite.

Attending a course on sexuality or reading one of the better sex manuals should be considered an essential preparation.

Many of the sexual problems of people with disabilities have no direct connection with the effects of their disability.

However, should the difficulties be caused directly by the disability, as, for example, impotence caused by nerve damage in spinal injury, the client needs to have not only that information clearly explained but also the opportunity to explore other means of sexual expression. To pursue the example of spinal injury; at its worse, loss of voluntary movement and sensation make penetrative genital intercourse impossible. However, kissing, stroking and fondling parts of the body where feeling is intact can give great physical pleasure and some people are able to achieve orgasm in this way.

People who have loss of sensation from chest level, for example, may discover that feelings of intense pleasure similar to those experienced in sexual excitement can be evoked in the area of skin immediately above the level at which skin sensation ceases. If the upper chest and back is stroked, kneaded and kissed these feelings can intensify to the point of extreme pleasure and subsequent release, as in orgasm.

It is, of course, of equal concern to men disabled in this way that they are unable to penetrate their partner. This is when oral or manual sex needs to be explored.

To be able to satisfy a partner by using the mouth, hands or even a mechanical aid such as a vibrator can give a man who is disabled great happiness. Similarly, a woman who is unable to tolerate penetration due to disability can enjoy close physical relationships and bring her partners to orgasm by masturbation.

To tell anyone disabled in this way, or their partner, that their sex life is necessarily over is not only cruel, it is incorrect. To help them consider how they and their partner can satisfy their needs for sharing sexual expression, and perhaps give permission to try new ways of loving, can be enormously helpful.

HIV AND AIDS

The general lack of information for pupils in Special Needs Schools and public ignorance about the HIV virus and AIDS related diseases in spite of media coverage, means that some people with disability are at risk. The assumption that people who are disabled are by definition not sexually active and the unwillingness to believe that sexual abuse and rape do occur may deprive someone who is disabled of information and possible counselling. The counsellor needs to be aware of this and to explore possible resources for help.

SPOD

The Association to Aid the Sexual and Personal Relationships of People with Disability is an organisation producing information leaflets, counselling by letter or telephone and training in issues related to sexuality and disability.

There is an accredited register of counsellors working in various parts of Great Britain to whom it may be possible to refer clients.

Anyone who feels the need for detailed help or information can contact SPOD or suggest their client does so. However, we would repeat that the majority of clients who are disabled need counselling for sexual problems that are no different from those experienced by people who are able bodied and having difficulties in their relationships.

The skills involved for the counsellor are the same.

SURVIVING ABUSE

Anyone, at whatever stage of their life, who is abused physically, emotionally or mentally or by neglect, suffers some degree of trauma.

The effects of abuse can be very long lasting. There are cases on record of people in their seventies talking for the first time of sexual abuse occurring in their early childhood. The whole of their lives has been adversely affected with emotional problems preventing any rewarding relationships, creating difficulties with authority figures and colouring all their activities.

When the abused is a child or adult who is disabled it can be argued that the emotional trauma is likely to be greater.

Experiences of abuse for people who are disabled, as for the able bodied, embrace a spectrum ranging from denigration and so-called 'teasing', to neglect and sexual or physical violence.

The emotional damage due to denigration is discussed in Chapter Three. In this chapter we are briefly considering sexual and physical abuse.

Firstly, it occurs. Children and adults with physical disability or illness are abused. Studies in the United States suggest that between 30% and 70% of abused children had a pre-existing disability.

Such abuse is often not reported.

The abuser is often a member of the family, perhaps the primary carer, or the responsible care assistant. The stress for a carer when a child or adult is profoundly dependent can be extreme. Disappointment or guilt in having given birth to a less than 'perfect' child, financial or housing problems, the breakdown of family relationships, physical exhaustion, being 'trapped' in the home, may all contribute to the stress of a carer.

Intimate daily care and the dependence of the cared-for create both the opportunity and the climate for abuse.

There are almost unsurmountable difficulties in making an effective complaint, let alone such a serious one, about someone on whom the victim is dependent.

REPORTS OF ABUSE

Complaints may well not be believed, either because the listener cannot accept or refuses to believe that such abuse could occur or because of fear of the consequences of making such a complaint official.

The victim may not have the opportunity of communicating with anyone he feels would take action. When there are speech or language difficulties such contacts may be even more rare. A child or victim with learning difficulties may not have the vocabulary to describe the experience. An elderly or confused person may not be understood or have his complaint dismissed as 'ramblings'.

The victim may have been convinced by the abuser that reporting the abuse would result in punishment and castigation. Guilt about the abuse is often experienced by the victim who may feel that his inherent wickedness has encouraged it. The abuser will often tell the child, 'You *make* me do it to you'. Children with disability often feel responsible for that disability and the 'disappointment' of the parent, and believe that he needs to be punished by that parent.

Abusers frequently threaten their victims with further 'punishment' if they tell, or bribe with gifts or special 'love' and attention. 'It's our special secret' is a frequently reported phrase.

When the abuser is a parent, the child may feel a responsibility to protect the abuser from discovery. The child is convinced that he deserves punishment and that he has forced the parent into administering it.

Abuser and abused are often trapped in a mutual conspiracy of silence, sharing a special relationship with complex emotional interdependency.

COUNSELLING THE VICTIM WHO IS DISABLED

The effects of abuse are, as we have indicated, long lasting. Damage may be caused by an early childhood incident, by a long period of abuse or by current abuse — or by all three.

The need for counselling of disabled survivors of abuse seems obvious. The resources able to meet that need, however, may not be readily available.

There is a great body of knowledge about disability and an increasing body of knowledge about counselling the victims and survivors of abuse. However, as in other areas of counselling, there seems to be little marrying of the two. Counsellors with skills in the area of disability often have little experience in the area of abuse and vice versa.

It is important to overcome the fears that divide these areas of skill and to share knowledge and experience. Only then can we begin to meet the very real needs of children and adults with disability who have experienced abuse in the past and/or are the victims of current abuse.

ENCOUNTERING ABUSE

A counsellor learning of current abuse of a child, or who has cause to suspect it, *must* share this information with the appropriate authorities.

Most authorities concerned with children have their own clearly defined Child Protection procedure. Failing this, the Social Services, the Police or the NSPCC must be informed.

The child should be told what action is being taken; he will already have been told before counselling started that this is a case in which confidentiality does not apply (See Chapter Seven).

If current abuse is occurring with an adult, he should be encouraged and supported to report the abuse to the appropriate authority. This may be the Police or Social Services, Head of Care or Management; the client and counsellor together should make the decision.

The counsellor should offer to accompany the client or to pass on the information herself. The role of Advocate may be appropriate.

The counsellor should not inform anyone without permission unless such a reservation has been made clear in the contract regarding confidentiality. As we stated in Chapter Seven, a client who is disabled has the same rights of confidentiality as any other client.

In the case of an adult who has severe learning difficulties or is confused or mentally disabled by, for example, a stroke, head injury or senility, and is experiencing abuse, the counsellor may need to report it without the victim being able to give informed consent.

CONSEQUENCES OF ABUSE

A client who has suffered, or is suffering, abuse may experience life-long feelings of guilt, self-disgust, betrayal, fear, mistrust and anger, destruction of self-esteem, difficulty or inability in making trusting relationships.

The reasons for guilt and self-disgust we have mentioned.

Betrayal is that of trust and of the exploitation of vulnerability by someone seen as strong and clever. Children are usually taught to respect and obey adults, especially those in accepted positions of authority.

Fear may be of other people; a little girl abused by a male may grow up with a fear of all men. Fear of someone finding out may involve terror of punishment, blame or disgust. There is fear that the story will not be believed and the victim branded and rejected as a wicked and evil liar.

This is a very real fear as stories of abuse often stretch belief.

So the role of the counsellor when told of abuse is first of all to listen. To give permission, to empathise (however painful this may be) and to accept are basic counselling skills. They are vital in cases of abuse.

HELPING STRATEGIES

When someone is ready to disclose, flood gates of emotion may be opened. At the other end of the spectrum, hints, allusions, tiny snippets of information may be allowed to dribble through. Often this may be a testing, as though the client were asking, 'Will you still accept me if you know the truth about me?'

Counselling the victims of past or present abuse is a skilled process, but sometimes there will not be access to 'the expert'. As in other areas of counselling, disability may bar access to such help.

If the reader is the only helper available or is the primary recipient of an unmistakable disclosure, it will be apparent that considerable sensitivity and gentleness with empathy and listening skills are demanded. When the existence of abuse has been acknowledged between client and counsellor and non-judgemental warmth established or re-established, work can commence with perhaps the gentlest of prompts or permission giving.

In the case of the reader being the only counselling help available we list a few useful strategies for clients disclosing past abuse.

Remembering

Enabling the client to make contact with the period in his life when the abuse occurred is often a prerequisite to any further progress.

Remembering, for example, the house in which he was living at the relevant time, the school he was attending, perhaps may release less comfortable memories. Recalling the friends and relatives, the activities he enjoyed, a person in whom he might secretly have wished to confide. All these and other reminiscence are likely to assist in bringing to the surface the buried terrors of abuse.

Writing to the child

The client writes a letter to the Child he once was. The client may have a special name for that Child. He may want to write as an adult friend or loving parent. Whatever form the letter takes, it should be an expression of the awareness of the writer of what happened to the Child and should offer support and reassurance.

Reading such a letter, although written by himself, can help the client believe that such acts did really happen. Often the enormity of the abuse and possibly past rebuffs when attempting to disclose the facts can lead the victim to doubt his own memories. He may come to believe that he has somehow invented the whole appalling story. Seeing in writing what he experienced confers validity. The counsellor's acceptance of the truth when she sees it written as well as having heard the words also helps combat the feeling of disbelief for the client. It often happens that 'new' facts are disclosed in such a letter.

Accepting the identity of the Child allows the writer to experience the enormity of the acts and to realise that guilt on the part of the victim is not appropriate. Reading the letter can enable the damaged Child within the client to hear good and loving messages.

Writing to the abuser

The client writes a letter to the abuser, expressing his feelings about what has happened. Very occasionally, the client may wish to send this letter if the abuser is still alive. More rarely such a letter may result in a verbal or written acknowledgement of the abuse and an apology. More often it offers a valuable way of exploring and owning emotions that are very painful to consider. Seeing the facts in writing and choosing the words to write is a cathartic experience and validates the client's feelings.

Sometimes writing with the non-dominant hand enables the client to disclose feelings 'censored' by the conscious mind. This strategy is well worth trying if the client is blocking written expression but wants to write.

Writing a story or fantasy

Writing or verbalising a 'story' of a visit to scenes where abuse occurred with the writer as a caring adult accompanying the abused Child can help the client recognise painful feelings at a safer distance. The client can express violent or 'unacceptable' fantasies of hatred or revenge which can be liberating.

One client with an acquired disability, writing to her Child about such a fantasy visit, described the glee they both felt in hitting their father's penis (which he had displayed on the Child's bedside table) with a heavy metal bar. She was able to laugh at the fantasy and then, for the first time, was able to describe the use to which her father had put such a bar in horrific abuse.

Allowing anger

The client is encouraged to express anger that is apparent in his voice or body when describing incidents of abuse. 'Bad language' is accepted and encouraged, as are threats of violent revenge or punishment of the abuser. The release of sometimes extremely powerful rage and its acceptance by the counsellor can assuage the guilt such feelings often engender and is a valuable catharsis.

Self-pity

Self-pity, as we have mentioned in Chapter Three, is too often used as a pejorative term. It can be immensely valuable if the client is encouraged to feel pity and sorrow for himself and for what has happened to him and how it has affected his life. Acknowledgement of that grief can be affirming and healing.

Other survivors

Working in a group or simply meeting with other survivors can help reduce feelings of isolation.

Sharing our own pain

Listening to stories of abuse can be a painful and horrifying experience for the counsellor. Sharing that with the client while clearly accepting the client's truth conveys acceptance, validates the client's feelings and gives permission for the client to reveal more and experience his own feelings.

Sub-verbal counselling

Many of the strategies described in Chapter Thirteen have proved extremely valuable in enabling clients to express feelings and describe events that they find too painful or too frightening to speak of, or that they have effectively 'buried' from their consciousness.

ACHIEVING RESOLUTION.

Learning to place the responsibility where it so very firmly belongs — with the abuser — is probably the most significant milestone along the road to resolution. It is only then that the victim can begin to forgive himself for that which, in reality, he was never responsible for in the first place.

It is then that the victim can become a survivor.

10.

BEREAVEMENT

The participants in the taped counselling session that follows are both counsellors. Liz and Simon co-counsel and both have some experience in counselling in the fields of disability and illness.

A few months before this tape was made, Simon suffered a massive coronary occlusion. After a period in intensive care he was allowed to go home but was re-admitted to hospital soon afterwards.

After his second period in hospital he returned home and made slow but fairly steady progress.

In the counselling relationship, Liz needed to monitor continually how much she could 'allow' Simon to explore of his very strong feelings because he became breathless and distressed easily and rapidly tired.

We have attempted to indicate by punctuation in the transcription of the tape the many pauses and interruptions caused by Simon's breathlessness and fatigue.

It will also be apparent that Liz was also feeling considerable distress at Simon's condition. It seemed important to her to ignore her feelings at this time. It was one of the occasions when the requirement of congruence to share feelings with the client was clearly not appropriate. Liz used another supervisor to work on her own feelings of pain and inadequacy in this session.

Should the reader, like us, need to know 'the end of the story', Simon has made a remarkable, though obviously not complete, recovery. He and Liz have explored very fully the feelings and experiences, of this early counselling session with a client facing his own, possibly imminent, death (L = Liz, S = Simon).

L. Hi.

S. Hi, Liz. Come in. Sit down. It's good to see you.

L. That's right. There's all the banal things — like — you're looking better than you were when I last saw you . . .

S. Oh, come on . . .

L. I said they were banal things.

S. People tell me I'm looking — looking well. I look in the mirror and I look bloody awful. My face — my face is like an old man. Everyone tells me I look better . . . why do people pretend, say the same stupid things, when they know that I know . . .

L. I'm caught — caught in the trap — I need to get to know you.

S. [Very sharply] What do you mean, get to know me?

L. I mean — that — although the you I know is still there, and is still accessible, it feels like the difference is there, um.

S. I don't *want* them to be there. I want to be the me that I know. Look, Liz, if I can't be me then I don't want to be anything. I don't want to live so much that I want to change my whole lifestyle, be someone else. If I can't be me I don't want to be.

L. So being 'me' and living a different lifestyle —

S. I can only be me. If I can't be me I don't want to be.

L. Being me. I said a moment ago that the differences, that make me uneasy, that you can see — I'm not too clear what I mean, but . . .

S. I can't separate the physical me from the other me, the two go together — I want to be — I can't lead a life — I don't want a life and that's . . .

L. Are you talking about dying?

S. I am talking about *me* dying. Let's cut the euphemisms, yes? I am talking about me dying. And that's OK. Talking about it is OK. Talking about it is more than OK, Liz, it's essential, because there are some things needed to be done, they, preparations, things . . . If I'm going to die, and that's — that's — pretty likely, then I must somehow get a solicitor and get my will brought up to date, I need to get up and get it witnessed. That's really been the — the important. I must — I want to — either get into the office, somehow go, before I had a heart attack —

L. That's the first time I've heard you say that.

S. What?

L. A heart attack.

S. Well how — what?

L. Well, before 'it' happened, 'before I was ill' . . .

S. Well I've got past that stage, I don't need that, I don't need those euphemisms any more. People don't understand that, that *I* can talk about it. People are treating me as if I'm some different being; some people are saying that I've changed generally — that's the trouble, they're not bloody saying, but they're implying, by their attitudes — they won't let me talk about it, about the heart attack, they won't use the words, they talk in polite terms, in hushed voices — they're saying as you did when you came in, *you*, you of all people came in and said I'm looking better, I'm not bloody looking better, I'm not . . . And other people say, tell me not to worry, I'll be alright, I'm — they're — not facing the real issues — if I walk — across — the room — for God's sake, it's difficult enough to walk across the room — people are either — looking at me — or — they're very consciously *not* looking — they're waiting to pick me up if I fall over — if — if I fall over — I bloody fall over, what's the — the —

L. Can I cut across here, because I'm beginning to get a bit confused, I want to sort out . . . well there's several — one thing is, there's almost a direct contradiction and I think it's maybe one to sort out for yourself because you started off by saying that your physical you was you, and you couldn't be you if they were stopping you doing things. That you didn't want to go on living, that you would rather die than not be the physical you that you have been.

S. That's right. And it's not just that —

L. No —

S. Because the physical part is an integral part of the rest of me —

L. Of the rest of you. Yes. Then, a little while later, you were saying it's not the physical things, the physical things aren't important, it's the way people are treating you.

S. Yes.

L. And you then went on to describe other people's attitudes, my attitude, which felt to me like people putting restrictions on you, guarding you — fussing you? . . . What I'm not clear about is what is threatening the person that is you, *is* it the actual physical limitations that you are left with after the heart attack, walking across a room is difficult, that getting agitated about things has a physical effect on you, or whether it is other people's towards that —

S. I can't disentangle those, they're all tied together —

L. Mm—hm.

S. It's bloody awful trying to get upstairs. If I — I — go up all the stairs — into my — bedroom — when I'm going to bed — at night — like half-past five or six — been up since — midday — If I — go into the bedroom first, get undressed — go back to the — bathroom — I don't have strength enough to walk back to — the bedroom — I have to crawl — can you imagine what that does to me? Can't you understand — I — oh — I — if I wash my face in the bathroom I have to sit down in the chair — Don't just say that 'Mm—hm', that *hurts* — it bloody *hurts* — it — I don't want to live like that — but no one will let me *say* these things. I *want* to cry, and — and — nobody will let me — say how awful it is — nobody will let the tears come — if only I could tell someone I need to die because I can't live like this. They won't let me get in touch with a solicitor, to get my bloody will written. They won't let me get in touch with the office, or even ring. I — I — I —

L. I hear, I hear you saying. I feel your hurt, distress,

S. Yes . . .

L. I hear the condescension, the lack of recognition of your pain, your needs.

S. No one lets me —

L. No one lets you —

S. My life — all my life — I've needed to — to support other people. To be — the one — that's there. For people to cry to. And now . . . I can't cry — not because of me — because of *them* — I can't cry because it hurts other people —

[At this point a group of children went past the house, shouting and singing 'Nick nack Paddy wack' very loudly.]

It's nothing to do with — what it does to me — I'm still, even now — expected to remember — other people's feelings — and respect them — I'm not doing it very well, but that's how it feels, what it feels is being demanded of me — Those BLOODY kids outside, they're just singing 'This old man'. This old man! I'm *not* an old man. I want to be out playing with those kids, I don't want to be the old man sitting in at home, and — if I can't do — that — I don't want to live — not — want — to —

L. Everyone else, still making demands on you, not allowed to cry or mourn because of how it makes them —

S. Because it hurts them.

L. Mm.

S. And at the same time caring for me. And doing it in the most *clumsy* — clumsy manner — that can only make it worse for me, being careful what they say to me — then — I'm sure they don't mean — but the hurt — that they cause me by fussing — not using the right words, by — looking at me,

— and if I dare to react to that, dare to — snap, snap back, to — to — remotely complain — the martyred looks, — the — gentle saintly sighs, the turning of the other cheek, the, the — doesn't anybody understand what any of those things *do* to me? Liz, can't people see that inside I'm — I'm still the same person? I haven't lost my sensitivity, do they think I don't *know*? What they're going through? Can't — can't they begin to see what *I'm* going through? Isn't there room — anywhere — for me?

L. I can only tell you — I can see — the hurts . . .

S. I don't *want* to be 'a heart patient' — you know, when I was, in hospital — nurses — all frightfully jolly, physiotherapists, well, physiotherapists telling me how many steps I could walk down the ward. The — triumph — of going to the loo — the first time, getting to the lavatory — by myself — Nobody *understanding* that — nobody understanding that — utter triumph — that was, of actually sitting on — the loo instead of — the humiliation of a bedpan — nobody understood that that was a triumph. Nobody understanding the humiliation of having a catheter inserted — in my penis. Not even having the control — to have a pee — when I wanted to. Why couldn't they understand that that was a humiliation, that things were being taken from me? My — bits of *me* were being taken away? No—one understands *now*, that when they treat me like — like a child — that has to be humoured — they are denigrating me. I'm a grown man — most of me is — I believe I have the right to make decisions. I want to make the decisions, I want to talk about them, I want to be sure I do the right thing, I want my wife to be able to drive the car properly, so that when I die she's not — restricted. I want — to — it's such a simple thing, I've got some money in a building society, and it's a joint account so that both of us have to sign — I want that joint account altered — so that — my wife can draw the money immediately — so that she — financially she'd be all right.

L. Yes . . .

S. Local authority pension schemes are good — but, you know, that's going to take a few weeks — or months — she's going to need money there and then and I said get the forms so that that's altered, and she won't get around to doing that — telling me I shouldn't talk like that. Why shouldn't I talk like that, if I'm going to die it's *me* that's going to die it's not them — why — c — why can't I — organise? It's so — simple it's — so — obvious — to do that sort of thing. I *know* I'm not the me I was — GOD that hurts to say — but there's still some of me inside — can't people recognise that little bit that's left? I . . . just don't want that bit of me to die — don't want to do anything to make me die. I've been in that scene before — this is different — Went for a walk outside yesterday — to the corner of the road, do you know how far that is? It's — probably — what, 20 yards? Certainly no more — so what do I do? — I have to — to find a wall [he is sobbing] to sit — down — to get my breath back — back again — and people — people *looking* at me — somebody — somebody I know quite well — saw — saw me — me sitting there and — and — crossed the road —

L. Where I feel the contradiction is, a few minutes ago you were talking about nobody recognising or trying to see how the physical alteration has changed the essential you, and now you are saying no one seems to see that you are still there, and the humiliation and frustration of them not acknowledging *that* you — *that* you, as you said — who is not able to walk to the end of the road. It seems to me there are so many contradictions for you, so many things happening at the same time, so —

S. Don't condescend to me, what do you bloody expect? Liz — until two months ago, I was an active fifty-four-year-old. Contemplating going — in just a couple of days — not contemplating, actually going — away with a crowd of kids, camping — in the Wye valley — um, rock climbing, canoeing — and —riding — very active — camping expedition — and NOW! I can't walk to the end of the road and you expect me not to have contradictions?

L. I don't think I said anything about expecting you *not* to have contradictions. I was trying to recognise what is around —

S. Of *course* there are contradictions — I don't want to be like this. If I can't be me I want to die — I don't want to live — I don't mind the time — it's only a matter of timing anyway — but there isn't too much left I want to — There's one or two things I want to — wait for. My eldest son, he and his wife — told us — two weeks ago — I'd like to wait and see his baby — I would like to wait around long enough to see my other son — home — from abroad. But I suppose that's really selfish — I would like to have seen him, though.

L. You said that you weren't going to do anything active to make yourself die. It feels to me like you've acknowledged doing exactly the opposite. Is it the baby, or your younger son coming home that you're fighting for — or are you fighting for yourself?

S. I don't know. I don't know.

L. Because the strong thing that's coming to me, is that you're fighting. You're fighting the bit that's wanting to die. It feels to me that it's the *me* we're talking about that's fighting, and that's waiting for —

S. I want to live — but I don't mind dying. Both. At the same time, I want to live and I don't mind dying. Certainly that first day, when I had the heart attack, when I was in hospital, certainly I was fighting then. Yes, I still want to live. There's so much joy — all the joy — like waking up and seeing my son there. It even registered on their machine, that joy. But dying's all right. But I really do need to make all the preparations of my life.

L. Yes.

S. And people must not stop — I don't want people to stop me doing *anything*. If I can do it I'll do it — and if I can't I bloody can't anyway. It's more clear to me now.

L. Yes. It's clear to *me* now that you are very tired.

S. Oh Liz, *so* tired . . .

L. I will come again as soon as it's OK.

S. No, not as soon as OK, that's not good enough. I need to — know when, I need something to hang on to.

L. Right. I could come Friday around four. If that's OK.
S. That good. Liz, I know we — we don't say, thank you — but I need to say it, to say thank you.
L. Thank *you*. Friday at four.

Selections from the following letter are used at the suggestion of both Simon and Liz. Both the letter and the transcript, together with some discussion with the participants, form the basis of the comments which follow the letter.

Dear Liz,

Thank you for your letter. I am, of course, very pleased that you would like to have the transcript of that session of two years ago used for your colleagues' book. It also occurred to me that you might be interested in hearing how it feels, two years on.

I remember that session with you very well. I remember the emotion bubbling out of me, rather like a saucepan of milk boiling over. There was so much hurt and pain and anger that, like the heated milk, it could not be contained within the normal boundary. Yet for most of the time to other people that is exactly what had to happen. To have overflowed to anyone else, as I did to you in those weeks after my discharge, would have been destructive and would have been cruel. If it were not for those sessions there would have been nowhere for that great welter of emotion to go.

I remember too, the pain of that session, the transcript you sent me reincarnated much of that.

There was the actual physical pain of talking for that length of time. I can recall the shortness of breath, and the general weakness that I knew then. I can also recall the fear that this engendered. You see, I did not know, at the time, how fully I would recover. No one had told me how much I might expect to regain of my former strength and ability. Or if they had I hadn't heard. What I did know was that living, permanently, in that state of weakness I could not tolerate.

During that session with you, then, I experienced the physical pain and its associated fears.

I also felt a considerable degree of emotional pain. This, in my remembrance, concerned bringing to the surface much that I had felt obliged to bury during the previous months.

It is difficult, even at this safer distance, to describe. It was, however, something like wrenching from deep within myself, parts of my actual body. My perception, now, is that I was giving you these pieces of myself to examine, seeking your agreement to discard them.

By far my most vivid perception, though, of that session is my utter relief at it being over. I do hope that you will not misunderstand that. What I am trying to convey is that the relief of having that surgery performed was enormous. I felt cleansed. As though the filth of the previous months had been washed away.

I do not mean, of course, that all the anger and hurt had disappeared, or that something had been 'magicked' away. Indeed a lot remains with me still. What had happened, though, was that an outlet had been found.

It is sad that those bad feelings cannot be drained away totally. I still have some hurt, some anger. I grieve for those things I can no longer do. Indeed I grieve for things I would never have done anyway.

I suppose I am grieving for the lack of choice. I retain the hurt and anger and I suppose that this retention has positive aspects too. Anger can be a constructive emotion, and in this context can be the spur to achievement in areas unthought of before my heart attack.

At the time of the taped interview, I was feeling negative about most things, certainly about myself. I was less of a person, I was damaged goods. I was too weak for most things; what strength I had was being used to the full in simply staying alive.

I was useless.

Had I been told then, that my contribution could be used to help write a textbook on counselling, then I would have been given some value, some worth. To have known then that I was still of some use to someone, somewhere, would have been a gift beyond price, and I regret not having received it.

All good wishes,

Simon.

DISCUSSION

As we stated at the beginning of this chapter, the transcript and the letter have both been fully discussed with the people involved in that co-counselling relationship. It is important to look at the difficulties and advantages of the co-counselling experience in the session recorded.

For Simon, it felt that Liz was the only person to whom he could disclose his feelings of grief, anger, frustration and confusion. Simon felt that Liz would understand his feelings and cope with his anger and deeply negative thoughts. It is worth noting that in this session Simon for the first time referred to his illness as a heart attack, and with her encouragement used the words death and dying instead of avoiding such unequivocal references.

Simon was also able to express some of his anger by directing it at Liz, when she appeared to repeat some of the insensitive remarks made by other people. He felt safe that she could take his anger and would not reject, reproach or patronise him. That was important and valuable to him.

For Liz it was more difficult. Simon's heart attack and his subsequent extreme weakness, the very real fear of his dying, had been a great shock and grief. To allow him to talk about his own death and his own anguish was not easy, and not to be congruent and share her own feelings was alien to their previous co-counselling relationship. The real need to monitor and control the extent to which she could allow Simon to express feelings that were affecting him physically was difficult and again alien to the way they were used to working.

The main skills apparent, then, in this session were those of reflection and clarification, but mostly reflection. It might be valuable for the reader to return to the transcript and to identify where Liz was reflecting and to observe when this enabled Simon to explore further.

For example, near the beginning of the session Simon says, 'Look, Liz, if I can't be me then I don't want to be anything.'

During the subsequent conversation, Liz reflects this repeated statement until she eventually feels able to confront Simon with the clear question, 'Are you talking about dying?'

Simon then is able to state clearly the practical details he feels are vital, and feels he is being deliberately frustrated in achieving. He knows that Liz will not fob him off with the dismissive and patronising refusal to listen he feels he has experienced elsewhere. He is also enabled to use the words 'before I had a heart attack', instead of his previous denying phrases, 'before it happened', and 'before I was ill'.

Using the stark and uncompromising words of disease, bereavement, mutilation or rejection is often the first step towards achieving some resolution of the problems they cause.

Simon's letter, written immediately after he had read the transcript for the first time and relived that experience of two years previously, reveals both how far he has come in his resolution and how vulnerable he still is to those early feelings. He is able to discuss how responsible he felt for the feelings of those close to him, and how angry and rejected he felt that no one appeared to recognise how little he was able to take that responsibility. He is able to recognise clearly his needs at that time and to assess how far the counselling session went in meeting them.

One of the aspects that Simon did not seem to appreciate, even in this letter of two years later, was the extent of the emotional needs of those who were trying to care for him. Perhaps it is worth reiterating that Simon is himself a counsellor of many years' standing, and therefore not without his own self-awareness. He recognised that, in his own crisis, he needed help. Because, perhaps, of the magnitude of the crisis for him, Simon uncharacteristically neglected the needs of those who were caring for him, indeed he disparaged their efforts. He appeared to be so engrossed in his own condition and his feelings about it, that he ignored the feelings of those around him.

It may be, in such circumstances, that members of the caring professions could give permission to the relatives of patients to talk about their own feelings.

It may also be true that members of the caring professions will recognise the attitude that Simon displayed in some of their own patients, and it may be that they will also be able to recognise the effect that this has upon themselves.

Towards the end of his letter, though, it is apparent how much of that early anger and grief is still close to his consciousness. Despite the fact that he and Liz have since explored very fully her feelings about Simon's illness, nowhere in the letter does he acknowledge this. He seems too close to those old angers and resentments, and his outburst at her omission in telling him of a possible use for the tape is uncharacteristic of their usual working relationship. It would seem that there would be some value in him and Liz working on the resentment expressed and discovering its true nature.

We are not presenting this taped counselling session as an example of 'how it is done', nor as a guideline on the feelings of a patient facing his own death. What we feel is its value is as an example of the need for a client to explore and express his feelings in a safe situation, and of the counselling skills that can enable this to happen. It is an example of how this piece of counselling was done and how one person felt about his severe limitations and possible death.

We also hope that Simon and Liz have demonstrated clearly both the need for, and the value of, counselling.

We have written of the bereavement of loss, some of the feelings surrounding the loss of health and status and the similarity that these may have to the feelings present in actual bereavement — that is, when someone close to us dies.

Text books and articles about bereavement abound and most mention the stages through which many people travel before arriving at some form of resolution. These are often listed as Denial, Anger, Grief, Depression, Bargaining and, eventually, Acceptance.

While these emotions are also likely to be experienced by a newly disabled person, there may be differences and a different emphasis. It seems unlikely that Ben will ever come to acceptance of his changed conditions and life-style.

It is important to be aware of the emotions people are likely to experience following the death of a loved one, if only to be prepared for the strength of these feelings on occasion. It is probably in this field of counselling that listening skills are at a real premium and when the true value of creative listening is most apparent.

A volunteer working with a Bereavement Project said of her first visit to a client, 'When I was approaching her house I was asking myself what on earth I was doing there, and had thoughts of quietly making my way back to the bus stop and going home. As it happened, as soon as my client opened the front door she began talking about her sorrow and loneliness over her husband's death and for the next hour she hardly paused for breath. I realised I did not have to be an Anna Freud or Mother Teresa to be effective — simply to be there and listen was enough.'

So often friends and family do not allow the bereaved person to talk and express how they truly feel, when perhaps this is their greatest need. This may be from a compassionate desire to protect (who is being protected?) from embarrassment at a display of painful emotion or from a feeling of inadequacy, of inability to 'make it better'. If the pain is not talked about, it will go away.

Many people as children were told not to look at nasty things, such as a road traffic accident or something rather unpleasant on the pavement. It seems almost as if this attitude continues into adult life, including the bereavement of a friend or relative. If we don't talk about it, it may go away. If I don't allow the bereaved person to talk about their feelings they won't become hurt or upset by those feelings (and, perhaps more significantly, neither will I).

This can sometimes be taken to the extreme of ignoring the subject altogether or of cutting the bereaved person out of our life completely, as though the pain that person is suffering is contagious.

A young women who was grieving the death of her baby son said bitterly, ' I have suddenly become invisible. When I walk down the road even people I thought were my friends don't see me, they even cross over the road when they see me coming'.

Counselling in bereavement is invaluable for anyone going through the process of grieving. People's needs may be different: some need to weep, some to express anger about the death — or about the dead person for leaving them. They may want to talk about the person who has died or discuss the problems of life without them. Resolution may come quickly or take many years. Feelings may become acute at times of anniversaries or celebrations or memories of these times may provide comfort.

Counselling gives the client permission and space to experience and express their feelings without pressure to conform to someone else's perception of how, and when, they should react to their bereavement.

BEREAVED CHILDREN

If adults are sometimes denied permission to express their grief for fear of hurting the listener, it is perhaps even more true of children. The facts of death are often concealed from them and their needs in bereavement denied.

Children, including very young children, need to be helped to understand death in simple language and with examples they can cope with. Secrets, myths and half truths can be a great deal more frightening for children than reality.

There is a saying that 'Death is a Fact of Life'. Children need clear information about the facts of life and whereas fairy tales about gooseberry bushes and doctors bags can cause confusion and risk, the myths of death can cause terror. A child informed that someone 'went to sleep and didn't wake up' was terrified of going to sleep herself and also had nightmares about her parents never waking up.

Children in a school for children with special needs were never told of the death of a classmate — the child was simply never mentioned again. The headteacher said that he was protecting the children from fear and unhappiness. A new teacher mentioned to her class that a former member of that class had been in her previous school and talked about him. She was puzzled by the reaction of her pupils who were exchanging bewildered looks and muttering to each other. Finally one blurted out, 'But he's dead!' When the teacher asked why on earth they had thought that the children told her, 'When people in this school die no one talks about them, they just disappear. We don't ask because they just say they've gone to another school. We thought Russell was dead'.

Three-year-old Lucy was told that a favourite aunt was so ill in hospital that she had gone to heaven. It was some time before it was realised that Lucy did not believe this. In her perception, Auntie could not have gone up to heaven from her hospital bed because she would have bumped her head on the ceiling.

Half truths can lead to confusion!

Children who are given the facts and loving support are able to achieve their own resolution.

Samantha was six, she was a twin and her sister was very severely disabled. Her parents were separated and, although her mother sometimes had difficulty in coping, there was a warm and loving extended family who offered considerable support. The absent father saw Samantha on an irregular basis and she loved him dearly.

Sadly, he died in quite tragic circumstances.

The initial reaction of the whole family was to cover up his death as much as possible and there was an agreement to tell Samantha that her daddy had gone away 'for a long, long time.' After talking with her counsellor, however, the mother decided to tell the truth in terms that Samantha would be able to understand.

Samantha's mother told her that Daddy was too ill to be made better on earth and had gone to heaven to be looked after by Jesus.

A few weeks later, Samantha did a painting at school. There were two stars in heaven, a large one, which she said was her daddy, and a small one. The smaller one, she said, was her baby cousin who had died some eighteen months previously. She had never been told of the death of her cousin and the family had assumed that Samantha had forgotten her.

Somehow this six-year-old had worked it out for herself, but had colluded with adults in not talking about it. That seems an intolerable burden to place on a child. Children as much as adults listen to what is not being said and draw their own conclusions.

Fear and confusion result from secrecy, prevarication and half truths. Guilt is often a corollary of fear and confusion.

Many people feel guilt at the time of a death and wonder if some sin of omission or commission has somehow contributed to the death. These feelings are certainly experienced by children. Children observing adults who are clearly suffering from strong feelings may not always be able to identify those feelings (grief can often be interpreted as anger) and an atmosphere of secrecy can easily feed guilt.

In Chapter Thirteen we describe how the son of a woman with acquired disability became convinced that he was the cause of his mother's illness (and that of two other loved family members). Children (and indeed some adults) may easily come to feel that they are responsible for the death of someone that they may have had angry feelings about or neglected. Honesty about the facts of death and the opportunity to talk about it and ask questions will help a child come to terms with death.

There is some indication that Samantha reached a healthy resolution of her grieving for her father. A little over a year after his death she was taken to Ireland to visit his grave. She decided without any prompting to bring back a pebble from his grave and it is now among her other treasures on a shelf beside her bed.

THE DEATH OF A CHILD

The death of a young child is often the most difficult to cope with. Parents and other family members are frequently in need of particularly sensitive counselling. Facing the reality of what has happened is essential as is gentle support and understanding.

To see grieving parents holding in their arms the body of their dead child is heart rending but it is essential for them to be able to say goodbye. Parents who have been denied the opportunity to see and hold the body of a stillborn baby or miscarried foetus talk of anguished feelings that the very existence of their lovingly anticipated child has been denied. 'He was treated like a bit of rubbish' was the tearful remark of a woman who never saw her dead baby, miscarried over forty years before.

Without the goodbye, which is one of the major functions of all funeral rituals, the mourning process cannot progress and the bereaved may be trapped in a morass of grief.

Children facing their own death, children with terminal illness mourning their own bereavement, are discussed in Chapter Eleven.

MOURNING

Saying Goodbye does not mean that the person — child, adult or unborn baby — will ever be forgotten. This is not, and should not be, expected. Photographs, mementoes and memories are precious and should be valued and talked about. To do less is to deny the life of the person who has died.

The dead person can be likened to a thread in a tapestry, always there and a part of the whole, but not dominating the whole picture. The shortest of lives contribute a thread.

The stages of mourning are important to recognise, although obviously people do not progress through them in a neat and orderly fashion, either in order or to an ordained timetable. We believe that it is vital that people who are bereaved are given permission to talk and speak of their feelings at their own pace. This may include a great deal of repetition, it may include many disconnected memories, feelings of anger, resentment, anguish or depression, often merging with one another.

Unless there is skilled creative listening, unless accurate information is given and euphemisms avoided, resolution is likely to be delayed and the client's emotions further damaged. The use of such terminology as 'passed on', 'passed away,' 'gone over' or facetious phrases such as 'popped his clogs' are often a ploy to deny the reality of death and contribute to the fear and horror so often associated with dying. Simon expressed relief at being able at last to use the words 'death' and 'dying' when talking to Liz. The fact of death needs to be recognised and acknowledged.

Some of the sub-verbal techniques described in Chapter Thirteen may be helpful in bereavement counselling. Whatever methods are used it is important that the counsellor does not collude in fantasies about the person not having died but gone away on a long holiday or to live somewhere else. The words used by the counsellor need to be direct and, in the case of children or people with learning difficulties, may need to include information about death and dying appropriate to their understanding. The message, however, needs to be clear.

11.

COUNSELLING IN SOME SPECIFIC AREAS

ACUTE TRAUMA

Many of the conditions we have discussed in the context of counselling are long-term or gradual in their effect on the physical and emotional condition of the patient/client.

Sudden accident or injury can produce equally acute feelings. When such trauma affects a young person, particularly a physically active and energetic person, the very sudden transition from a life in which physical achievement was very important to one of dependence, pain and disability is intensely distressing.

Frequently, a young person very involved in physical expression has invested a high level of his feeling of worth and personal identity in the fitness and ability of his body. This worth and personal identity may even be a very practical factor, as in a professional sportsman or one who hopes to make at least part of his career as such.

To such a person, the feelings following an acute injury are very strong and highly confusing.

Anger at being the victim of whatever accident or trauma he has suffered is often not acceptable to the stereotype of a 'good sport' and may be suppressed. Fear of possible lasting disability may be regarded as weakness and a facade of cheerful acceptance is kept up. The distress of relatives and friends may result in an attempt to shield them from the distress the victim feels.

These strong emotions cannot be totally suppressed. The person closest to the victim may bear the brunt of the anger, frustration and resentment that are suppressed in public but may explode destructively in private. Others may treat those closest to him with a display of criticism and carping and continual demands that can destroy the closest of relationships, especially when those outside the relationship may see a charming and courageous person coping with his injuries in a remarkably positive way.

In such circumstances, we see the role of the counsellor as enabling and giving very positive permission to the client to express his feelings. The fear may well be the most difficult emotion for the young person to admit. Not only does he experience the fear of his own fantasies about the possible outcome of his injuries, but also the fear of asking about that outcome. The fear of asking may be of hearing his worst imaginings confirmed, or of not being able to believe that he is being told the truth. Enabling a client to express his fears may well be the most valuable contribution the counsellor can make to enable him to resolve his difficulties, but the professional may well find herself in a position of being asked for information she may not feel professionally able to give. In this case the authors believe that it is her place to pass on (with the client's permission if that is in the terms of the counselling contract and, if it is not, an assurance of positive support will usually enable the most diffident client to give permission) the client's need for information to the person who is in a position to give it.

The counsellor may well find herself in possession of information she does not feel professionally able to give the client when he asks for it. We would suggest that she first examines whether or not this assumption is true. It may be that confidential information regarding, for example, the client's prognosis could be shared with the client by the counsellor. The counselling relationship may well be the most appropriate one in which the dreaded facts can be imparted and explored. This is not, of course, an easy role for the counsellor when the prognosis is not good or when the client's expectations are unrealistic. It can be even more difficult when the prognosis is uncertain.

The counsellor should perhaps explore her own feelings about where her responsibility to her client lies. If she comes to the conclusion that his questions would be best answered by her, we suggest that she approach the appropriate person or people and offer to undertake this task in the context of the established counselling relationship.

Should the client/patient not have been given the space and permission to experience and express his negative feelings and feels forced to suppress them, depression may result.

This depression may be overt and easily recognisable or it may be disguised. When depression is disguised it is all too easy to play along with the patient's assumed role. His asking may be disguised and devious. The counsellor will need to be very alert for any sign of a request for her skills and to respond sensitively.

THE ELDERLY

Simon's anger and indignation when he identified himself in the words of the children's song, 'This old man', and his anguished rebuttal, 'I'm *not* an old man', had little to do with his actual age. It was rather a denial of what Simon associated with the words 'old man'.

Many people whose chronological age would undeniably place them in the category 'old', whether this is disguised as 'senior citizen', 'pensioner' or 'geriatric', would vigorously deny the description. One of the authors remembers the outrage of a grandfather admitted to the 'old people's ward' of his local hospital. He wanted the family to put right what he saw as a totally inappropriate placement. He was eighty-three years old.

Most of us experience some problems as we grow further away from youth. These may be problems of unfulfilled ambition and the realisation that adolescent dreams are unlikely to be achieved. There may be disillusionment as we realise that the state of being adult, which looked so desirable from the viewpoint of a child, has its own problems and frustrations.

Physically most of us reach, or will reach, the stage when we are made to realise that some activities or physical skills we have taken for granted become more difficult or even impossible.

Many of us carry the body image of a much younger person and the sudden insight that others see us very differently can be an unwelcome shock. One of us remembers the outrage felt when a host indicated a comfortable chair and said, 'Let the youngsters sit on the floor'. The recognition that most of those present were at least 15 years younger (than myself) did not help at all.

When one is vigorous and alert, signs of approaching age can be difficult to accept. When illness or infirmity exaggerate the physical and/or mental deterioration of old age the bereavement is severe.

Not only has the elderly person to learn to come to terms with his loss of ability but, all too frequently, with the insensitive and patronising attitudes of those around him.

The affront to dignity and self-respect of being referred to as 'Dad' or 'Ma', or, even worse, as 'Grandad' or 'Nan' is in no way compensated for by the kindness that often lies behind such appellations. Neither is the frequent use of given names, especially with a generation to whom the use of a title and surname is assumed and the use of a given name regarded as very disrespectful, any more acceptable.

The loss of dignity and self-respect is all too often a feature of the elderly person's experience of hospital treatment and care. Often brought up in a society and time where the body was never exposed even to a loved partner, the violation of personal privacy can be acutely distressing. Even when the necessary attentions of nurse, doctor and therapist can be accepted, other affronts can be intensely humiliating. Far too often it is possible to see an elderly patient being wheeled along hospital corridors skimpily clad in a hospital gown, clutching an inadequate blanket in an attempt to preserve some dignity. The authors have seen elderly ladies with their legs ruthlessly exposed in a public area as a doctor or therapist assesses their gait or checks a prosthesis.

Sudden illness and disability, as in cerebrovascular accident, can add disorientation and bewilderment to the already heavy burden borne by the elderly patient. It is hardly surprising that many assume a grateful docility that may be at complete variance with their previous personality, whereas some may become demanding, cantankerous and unreasonable. The role of ward or department pet or mascot, or that of geriatric *enfant terrible* are perhaps familiar. It is salutary to realise how easy it is to stereotype the elderly patient and cease to assign to them the respect for an individual and valuable person that may be found easier to experience with the younger client.

Counselling the elderly client will often need to start by showing a respect for, and appreciation of, the abilities of a person who may see his abilities as inexorably diminishing. It may be necessary for that person's self-respect and sense of what is right and proper behaviour, that he does not share his feelings of grief and humiliation. Often though, when a counsellor who has established a relationship of respect and caring gives permission the client can express something of what he is feeling. This permission may be in the form of a disguised question, 'It must be very difficult for someone as independent as you to need help with this.' Permission may be equally effective given as a more personal comment, 'I don't know how I could cope with the frustration of not being able to do something I had done for myself for so many years'.

As when dealing with younger victims of speech-robbing illness or disability, it is always important to assume that the person to whom you are speaking is an intelligent and aware human being with the same need for dignity and self-respect as we have ourselves.

We will all, unless our lives are cut short by accident or illness, experience old age. We may regard this with dread, with resignation or even with anticipation. What is certain is that the quality of our old age will be affected not only by our health and financial circumstances but by the attitudes of those around us.

YOUNG CHILDREN

We will all, unless our lives are cut short by accident or illness, experience old age. We have all, without exception, experienced childhood. These experiences will have varied widely. What many of us will have in common is a memory of adults not listening to what we feel is important or of discounting our opinions and underestimating our perceptions.

Children, when we do listen to them and respect what they have to say, often demonstrate a level of understanding that confounds those who believe 'they are too young to be told', especially when the child is ill or has a disability. Answers and explanations may need to be simple but they should always be accurate.

Clare was just three years old when she asked through Blissymbols, 'Why me wheelchair?' She was asked, 'Do you want to know why you can't walk or talk? What happened to you?' She said yes, but looked a further question. She was then asked, 'Do you want to know why you and not other children?' She said yes again.

A child able to ask such questions was clearly deserving of answers. She was able to understand that 'the part of your brain that looks after the way your body moves was hurt when you were a little baby inside your Mummy,' at a level that satisfied her.

In response to the other questions, the counsellor told her that no-one knew why it had happened. It wasn't anyone's fault, no-one had wanted it to happen and no-one could have stopped it happening.

Clare was an intelligent little girl and over the next few years returned to her question again and again, wanting more information and testing adults' feelings about disability. She was also interested in how her peers felt about their disabilities. She was able to express her own anger and frustration and to deal with these distressing feelings.

George was nearly thirteen years old before he began to express awareness of differences between himself and his able peers. He had been a placid and undemanding child until adolescence aroused feelings of frustration when he asked questions and began to talk about difficult feelings.

However, at whatever age realisation occurs, a child needs to feel that he will be listened to and respected before he will communicate his feelings. A child, as much if not more than an adult, needs permission and trust before he can risk disclosing his thoughts and fears. He needs to be assured that anger and jealousy are not wicked feelings before he can express negative emotions.

John was six years old and his communication group were discussing 'feeling angry'. He said yes, he felt angry. He felt angry with his wheelchair. When he was asked if that was exactly what he wanted to say he said no, and when given a choice of other words chose 'disability'. Asked if there were any people he felt angry with he said 'me' and, after much hesitation, 'Mummy'.

John said he felt angry with himself because he could not do things. Further discussion led to a request from John that the counsellor help him tell his mother that he felt very angry with her that she had not prevented his disability.

The meeting with John's mother was an emotional one with both John and his mother expressing the grief and anger that they both felt. John's mother was able to assure him that she did not want another son but John, but that she, of course, wished that he was not disabled. John's beaming smile revealed that an unexpressed fear had been resolved — that his mother did not want him because he was disabled.

If Ben felt oppressed and guilty by the demands of others to be well-adjusted and cheerful, how much more intolerable are the same demands put on small children. Yet we do make such demands.

A crying child, when that child is disabled, it appears must instantly be comforted.

If a sweet or treat fails, a funny face or joke is ineffective, then it is assumed that the child has a pain or is uncomfortable. Appropriate action can be taken and we can avoid our distress at the idea of a child angry or unhappy because of something we cannot put right.

It is no coincidence that visitors to schools for children who are physically disabled almost always comment, 'They are all so happy!' Of course that is how they appear. It is what we demand of them, unrelentingly and remorselessly.

If this seems harsh, the reader has only to give the child space, understanding and permission to talk about their real feelings. Without demands to be 'happy' children can talk about other, more painful feelings. Then resolution can commence and a child who is real will emerge — sometimes happy, sometimes miserable, sometimes angry, sometimes full of joy. We will have the chance of meeting a perfectly normal child with the additional problems of disability or illness. These problems are not suppressed or discounted but can be resolved by the child as can those of the adult, with counselling enablement.

TERMINAL ILLNESS

It is perhaps in terminal illness that children have a great deal to teach us.

Some children, as some adults, do not appear to realise the nature of degenerative or terminal illness.

Peter was twelve and had Duchennes muscular dystrophy. He had deteriorated in three years from complete mobility to requiring an electric wheelchair. He could no longer even remove the cap of a felt pen to colour in his tiny, detailed drawings. However, when talking in group discussions Peter stated that he had been born disabled and had never been able to walk or use his hands.

Mrs Johnson was sixty and recovering from the effects of a fourth operation for a rapidly growing cancer. She talked cheerfully about her return to complete health.

Matthew also had Duchennes muscular dystrophy and was also twelve. He asked a teacher why no one would talk about death? She returned the question to him and he responded,

'Well, it's because they think I'm going to die, isn't it? Of course I am. But they can't say when, can they? Death stands behind everyone's shoulder. You might drive your little mini under an articulated lorry on your way home tonight! So why should people have to feel it's such a big deal for me?'

Frank was fifty four and had an inoperable tumour. He spent the time before his death putting all his affairs in order. He talked at length to his wife and three children, remembering good times and bad, and sorting out old grievances and misunderstandings. He contacted long neglected friends and spent time with those close to him. He talked about his grief and anger about his shortened life — mourning his own bereavement. He listened to the feelings of those around him.

For Peter and Mrs Johnson, their apparent lack of understanding about their situations may have been a coping strategy; in Mrs Johnson's case from an additional need to protect her family from distress. Paul may have learned in his turn from his family that there were subjects that must never be mentioned. We can never know.

Matthew and Frank chose to explore their own deaths and were both enabled and supported in doing so. Frank died peaceful in mind, although distressed in body, and his family were able to grieve without guilt. Matthew lived his short life to the full, dying very suddenly about three months after the reported conversation.

Of course, no-one should be forced into being the recipient of information he has not asked for and is not ready to receive. But no-one will ask if they are not given the space, permission and time to do so or the sensitive perception that recognises an indirect question.

Those working with children who have cancer almost invariably uphold the philosophy that children are given full information about their illness. Children in cancer wards sometimes shock the unthinking with their matter of fact acceptance of their condition. This is not because they do not understand the implications, but the opposite. **Knowledge is almost always less frightening than imagination or the speculation of ignorance.**

Bereavement when it is one's own death involves the same mourning process as any other bereavement. Frank said on a number of occasions that he was lucky in having the time to prepare for his own death. We do not feel we have the right to deprive anyone, child or adult, of that opportunity when such a chance is possible.

Ignorance breeds fear. We might ponder on the woman who said, on being told she had multiple sclerosis,

'Thank goodness. At last I know what is the matter with me. Now I can get on with living with it'.

12

RACE, CULTURE AND RELIGION

It is quite clear that any counsellor needs to be sensitive to the race, culture, gender, religion and language of her client. It is also to be hoped that the counsellor will have developed sufficient self-awareness to prevent overt racism, for example, in her practice or attitude.

However, it is our hidden prejudices and stereotypes that can sometimes find their way into our conversation and thoughts and take us unawares. This can best be illustrated by looking at the following overheard comments and reflecting upon what they say about the people who made them and their hidden feelings about certain groups of people.

'He won't be on time (laughing) *they* never are.' Therapist discussing a patient.

'Doesn't she look a typical client.' Social Worker.

'Of course, you have to remember she's hydrocephalic.' Counsellor discussing a client in supervision.

'Of course, their attitude towards their daughters is always restrictive.' Teacher about a pupil.

'He's very good-looking. What a waste he's a gay.' Conversation in nurses' staff toilet.

'Why should she be worried about sex, she's well over sixty.' Surgeon talking about a patient.

The reader could perhaps supply an ending to the phrase, 'He's a typical . . .'

If such comments could be made by people in the caring professions, as they were and are, one wonders how they will be able to cope when a client's culture conflicts with their own.

One of the authors, as part of the counselling process, was attempting to help an adolescent who was disabled, towards independence. This young person's family happened to originate from the Indian sub-continent. She told the counsellor that she had a deep love and respect for her parents and for her culture, but she had lived all her life in a Western society. She felt that her parents were being unrealistic in expecting her to conform totally to their way of life.

The counsellor's instinctive reaction was firstly that the parents were adding to their daughter's disability and secondly that the counsellor wanted to encourage the client towards total independence.

The dilemma for the client was that she was an adolescent young woman with disability, of Asian origin, living in a Western society, with peers she saw as enjoying a far greater degree of freedom. She felt a strong conflict between this and the love and respect she had for her parents and, indeed, for her culture.

Clearly her parents had a dilemma also. Not only did they have a young daughter who according to tradition needed to be loved, protected and held close within the family. This daughter was also disabled, a gift from God and therefore worthy of even greater protection.

The dilemma for the counsellor was also painful. There was a conflict between the counsellor's own prejudices and values, the quite cerebral acceptance of the family's values, and the wishes, fantasies and aspirations of her adolescent client.

For many of us it is too easy to fall into the trap of 'colour blindness,' to try to see everybody as the same, regardless of colour, race or creed. In fact, special consideration needs to be taken of what are sometimes very different attitudes, beliefs and values of people who come from a culture other than our own — wherever we happen to stand.

We are all different. To try to see everyone as the same is to deny that individuality. If a client has been raised in a religion or culture that is different from our own it is important to acknowledge this quite openly. Rogers's concept of congruence is appropriate here.

It also seems important to try to gain some knowledge and understanding of the particular culture of the client, if it is unfamiliar to us. Again, congruence can be useful.

As in every other aspect of counselling, it is essential for the counsellor to accept and value the uniqueness of each individual and the underlying humanity we all share. Perhaps it is also important that we value the achievements of other cultures and nations. It may be important in this context that the counsellor's self-awareness includes confidence in her own cultural identity, valuing this without denigrating or stereotyping other's cultures.

It is all too easy to categorise. Was Ben, in the euphoria he was expected to display, so often associated with multiple sclerosis, suffering from someone's prejudice and stereotyping? Could it be that Simon, so acutely distressed at being regarded as an old man, was reflecting some perceived assumptions about elderly people?

We feel it has to be recognised that all minority groups suffer a greater or lesser degree of oppression. Any person or group of people who are seen as different from the majority is likely to be mocked (Irish 'jokes') pitied (oh, the poor dear) or regarded as a lesser being (well, what else can you expect from . . .). The majority has the power. This clearly applies to people who are disabled as to any other group.

If a person who is disabled happens to belong to another minority group as well, be it ethnic, religious or linguistic, the likelihood of oppression is proportionately increased. In these circumstances an even greater degree of sensitivity, understanding and empathy is necessary if counselling is to be effective.

Coping with racism and disableism (or any other 'ism') is clearly an enormous burden and one of which we need to be acutely aware. The counsellor can profitably listen and learn from those disadvantaged by society in this way.

A client with severe learning difficulties was very proud of a teeshirt with the slogan,

'LABELS BELONG ON JARS — NOT PEOPLE'

13.

SUB-VERBAL COUNSELLING

We have so far described a counselling process which depends on the client talking to the counsellor, using speech or (in the case of the client unable to speak through disability) using alternative methods of communication.

However, there are times when the client has difficulties in expressing his thought and feelings. He may be blocking his understanding because of fear or pain. He may be unaware of his true feelings. He may find it impossible to verbalise feelings that are confused or obscure.

On the other hand, some clients are so verbally fluent, so skilled in self-analysis, so adept with words, that they become trapped in a flow of language that effectively disguises from them and from the counsellor the real feelings and thoughts.

For all these clients (and for almost every other client) what we have termed 'sub-verbal counselling' can be extremely valuable.

What do we mean by this term?

In Chapter Five, we described how a client became aware of, and was able to own, her feelings about her disability. By describing herself as an object in her home she was able to experience feelings of rejection and anger. Unable to describe her own feelings to the counsellor she was enabled when describing the 'feelings' of a kitchen stool.

This is one technique of sub-verbal counselling. Although the client was indeed using language, what she was expressing was something beyond the obvious demands of the exercise.

Sometimes the use of 'props', of a variety of materials, can release a client to experience and describe or demonstrate hidden feelings and memories. We will be describing some of these.

Sub-verbal counselling can therefore perhaps be defined as a technique for enabling the client to recognise and resolve feelings and problems using indirect means.

Sub-verbal counselling has proved very valuable when working with clients who are over-articulate and with those who have little or no use of language. It works with clients who are physically able and those who are totally disabled. The very young and the very old respond positively. Those who are 'stuck' or who are unable to own negative feelings can be enabled to move on, sub-verbal counselling can also be a short cut to subconscious memories.

Last, but by no means least, there is an element of play in many of the methods of sub-verbal counselling. The exercises can be fun and the release of Free Child (See Chapter Five, transactional analysis) means the release of deep-feelings that Free Child holds.

CHOOSING AND DESCRIBING

Use of material that the client can choose and talk about can release important feelings and memories.

Stones and pebbles we have found to be very powerful. Each of the authors has a collection of seaside pebbles, polished stones and pebbles picked up in parks and gardens. These are of a wide variety of shapes and colours.

A girl of ten with learning difficulties was reported as behaving in a very disturbed way. She was invited to play with the stones and to choose a stone for herself and each of her family and friends.

Typically in the use of stones, she seemed very clear in her choices, discarding stones until saying with decision, 'this is me.' Her choices made, she was invited to arrange the stones on the table top. Next she was asked to talk about the stones.

Her own stone was described as 'a little, little stone, sort of grey and easy to lose.' Her foster father was a large stone, and she giggled as she said, 'It's got a hole in it because he's holy, he's a vicar'.

The family were arranged in a close group, her stone alone on the outside. Only a friend was close, a cup-shaped stone because 'it looks like and ear an' she's a good listener'.

It was then suggested that she rearrange the stones how she would like to see them. This time the little grey stone was placed close to the 'holy' stone and the foster mother stone (a 'pretty, nice' piece of polished turquoise). The friend was at first placed close to this group, but then pushed vehemently aside and the child exclaimed 'I'm not having her big ear there, listening to everything I say'.

The counsellor reflected, 'She listens to everything?'

'Yes', said the child, 'She's nosy and horrible and I hate her'.

Further work disclosed that the friend, apparently a 'best friend', was in fact tormenting the client with tales that her foster parents didn't want her and that the friend had heard them say so. Once her fears had been confessed, the child was able to accept reassurance and to feel close to her foster family in reality.

Almost without exception we have found that people are fascinated with the stones and their choices are always made with decision. People with visual disabilities find great significance in the feel of the stones and those unable to handle the stones are equally decisive in their visual selection.

The value of the stones does not seem to be diminished when the client is aware of their use. Both authors have used stones in their own supervision and have discovered unexpected insights.

When using stones with a client the counsellor will, of course, have her own ideas as to why a particular choice has been made. However, as in other methods of counselling what is important is what the client feels are his reasons. The counsellor can by reflection lead the client into the exploration of his description and enable him to identify and own what he has revealed.

Fabrics. When elderly, confused people or those with Alzheimer's disease are encouraged to reminisce and so recover some of their own identity, pieces of fabric will often provide the trigger for a memory.

Fabrics can also be used in a similar way to the stones already described.

A collection of small pieces of a very wide variety of fabrics offering the client a choice of colour and texture can enable the client to choose and describe the qualities of his chosen material. Again, this can be an attractive activity. Again it can lead to valuable insights.

Colours and smells may be used if the counsellor is not prepared with a collection of stones or fabric. Inviting the client to choose, and describe a colour that they feel represents himself, another person or a situation can 'work' for some clients. For others, thinking of and describing an odour or scent can be enabling.

For clients unable to visualise in this way, offering coloured cards may help; it is more difficult but still possible to offer a variety of smells. As well as the problem of preparing a collection of odour impregnated materials it must be remembered that the sense of smell can quickly become saturated.

'I am . . .' In this exercise the client describes himself as, for example, an animal, a colour, a piece of furniture. He must do this in the first person and the present tense and what he describes must be true, for example, 'I am an elephant, I have tusks and a long trunk' is not true but 'I am an elephant, I am very strong but gentle unless I am very provoked' may well be.

Some clients find it easier to fill in a questionnaire, an example of which is given. Once completed the client is asked to talk about his choices.

IF I WAS A . . . I WOULD BE
Animal
Colour
Day of the week
Month of the year
Piece of furniture
Item of clothing
Room in the house
Type of weather
Means of transport
Flower or plant
Vegetable
Country in the world

Often the client is able to recognise clearly and comment on what these choices disclose about the way he sees himself or wishes he could be.

Miniature dolls. Particularly when working with children, miniature dolls can be very useful. Either a number of doll's house dolls, including plenty of all ages and sexes, or a set of faceless, stylised figures that can represent any person the client wishes may be used.

A description of a child using such dolls will be found in Chapter Eight. Sometimes improvised 'dolls' can be even more effective. Serendipity on an occasion when a counsellor found herself counselling a very well-defended 11-year-old-boy discovered the advantages of improvisation.

The boy was the son of a woman with multiple sclerosis. The mother felt her son was very disturbed by her disability and he was displaying behaviour towards her ranging from hysterical over protectiveness to open hostility and aggression.

He agreed to counselling but, although very articulate and intelligent, talking readily about his mother and himself, he expressed a very rational and philosophical attitude about her disability. When the counsellor reminded him that his mother was concerned about him he offered the theory that she felt guilty that he was suffering because of her disability and assured the counsellor that he understood and would try to reassure her.

After three such sessions the counsellor felt she must change her approach and suggested he talked a bit about his family. She proposed that he drew pin men on folded scraps of paper to represent each person so that they could keep track.

The boy drew, identified and arranged his folded papers. Asked to place himself in the centre, he put his mother, grandmother and grandfather very close, his brother, father and other family members further away. Invited to explain, he told the counsellor that those three were all sick or disabled and he felt very close to them. She said, 'So those closest to you are the sick ones?' and on impulse flicked over the three papers.

He reacted violently, grabbing the papers and carefully setting them up again. With tears pouring down his cheeks he said, 'Everyone I love best gets ill or disabled or something. It's not safe to love me'.

His guilt at being, as he saw it, responsible for his mother's disability and his attempts to prevent her further damage which he felt would be caused by her loving him explained his behaviour and he was able eventually to recognise this. He was also able to admit that he did not in reality possess the destructive power that had so terrified him.

His comment on the exercise was, 'It's really strange; just pieces of paper but when you knocked them over I felt as if it was real and all my feelings came up to the surface.'

Cardboard cut-out figures, either made by the counsellor or made or directed by the client, can be used in the same way.

Drawings and paintings. As well as using drawings or representations of people, freely drawing or, even more, painting, can help express feeling and explore emotions. Drawing with the non-dominant hand to produce, for example, a self-portrait frees the client from trying to produce an artistically acceptable picture. There is an important additional advantage. As suggested in Chapter Nine, using the non-dominant hand can avoid 'censorship' by the conscious mind and release helpful symbolism.

Finger painting, when the client uses fingers or a hand to produce swirls and patterns of colour, can be a valuable release and often triggers feelings and memories. Any part of the body can be used as a tool, or a wheelchair driven across paper on the floor. As long as the client is reassured about 'making a mess' and is able to wash afterwards, Free Child can be allowed to express himself without restraint.

Plasticene or clay can be used in the same way, clay probably being more therapeutic but plasticene easier to store and manage. The client may want to manipulate the material into random shapes but frequently the modelling of a human figure will result. Without encouragement the figure or figures can be identified and used to act out real or imaginary situations.

There is a very real safety in manipulating such figures and violent feelings can be acted on in destruction or mutilation of the figures, which can easily be restored afterwards. Anyone who has observed the relief and satisfaction demonstrated by a child squashing the clay model of a feared or hated adult into a shapeless lump realises the emotional release of such an activity. It works as well for adults!

Random objects. Externalising an account by using any objects available (the example of retired generals re-enacting battles on the dining table with salt cellars and wine glasses comes to mind) can lead to disclosure of deep and painful feelings.

Simon, whose story is recorded in Chapter Ten, demonstrated this vividly on one occasion.

Simon had returned to work in one of the caring professions after an excellent recovery from his heart attack. He was working in co-counselling with Liz.

Liz asked Simon to designate objects on a coffee table as members of his family. He selected the empty cellophane wrapping from a pack of biscuits to represent himself. He described the wrapping as being useful, as containing something sweet and nourishing, as being transparent so that everyone could see what was inside.

He then went on to choose and describe other objects and worked out a problem in family relationships that had been concerning him. When the exercise ended, he carefully replaced all the items. The cellophane wrapper he screwed up and threw into the bin with the comment, 'Well, that's just a bit of rubbish now, isn't it?'

Liz reflected, 'A piece of rubbish, no longer any use?'

'Well, yes.' said Simon. 'There's nothing left, is there?'

It was the end of the session and Liz felt that it was important to allow Simon his judgement as to that disclosure. However, she retrieved the cellophane from the bin, smoothed it out with great care and placed it carefully in her folder with the comment, 'Well, I think it's too valuable to chuck away.'

No more was said at the time but for Simon it was an important statement and affirmation.

Body sculpting. When working with a family or with a group of clients, body sculpting can be a valuable way of exploring and trying out relationships and situations.

The working client allocates characters to others in the group and arranges them in a 'sculpture' he feels expresses the situation he wishes to work on. He can comment on what he is doing. People in the sculpture may say how they feel in the position in which they have been put.

The client can then move characters to try different possibilities.

A useful additional prop is a collection of long lengths of elastic that can be used to connect people. For example, a social worker needed to make a difficult decision with a family which might have involved removal of one or more family members from the home. Each member of the family arranged the others in a sculpture and then rearranged the group to explore the different possibilities. The child in each case was connected to the parents with elastic and the tension of the elastic as different distances were attempted proved a vivid expression of the ties between them.

The exercise enabled each member of the family to express in a very tangible way his feelings and for the family and social worker to explore every possibility. It was also of great value to the social worker in reaching a decision.

Relaxation and creative visualisation. For many clients, teaching effective relaxation techniques can be a useful way of enabling the client to resolve stress, especially that caused by an intractable situation. Deep relaxation is much more than a physical rest. The planned setting aside of 20 minutes to half an hour to 'do nothing' implies that the client is valuable and deserves that time. It is possible to be proud of a new skill. The relief of the physical effects of stress frees the client to work towards resolution of the problems contributing towards that stress.

When deep relaxation is combined with creative visualisation the benefits are greatly enhanced.

To teach this technique, the client must first of all be comfortable, in a suitable position, either lying with whatever support is needed or in a reclining position. There should be no risk of interruption and reasonable quiet. If music or sound is used it should be calm and restful and of a volume to provide background sound only. Some excellent tapes for relaxation can be bought of both music and natural sounds such as sea waves.

The counsellor's instructions should be in a quiet, relaxed voice using calming repetition of phrases. Observing the client's breathing and timing instructions with the client's breath pattern is more effective than instructions to breathe at a particular rate; clients with cerebral palsy or heart conditions, for example, can find attempting to control their breathing the opposite of relaxing.

Similarly, the technique of first tensing, then relaxing muscles is often counter-productive with many disabilities. Using words such as 'floppy, soft, heavy' is more effective.

Frequent repetition of a word such as 'calm' or 'peaceful' when initiating relaxation prepares the client for the suggestion that he can use this word as a trigger whenever he wishes to re-experience the feeling of deep relaxation.

When the client seems relaxed creative visualisation can be introduced. The counsellor describes, using the same voice and repetition technique, a scene in a garden, by the sea or in the countryside. She can use her knowledge of the client in her choice, or follow her own preferences. The client is invited to experience with all his senses the placed described, always with the use of the chosen 'trigger' word. The client is described as being at peace in the place, without pain or stress, valued and loved. When the client is more experienced, specific suggestions can be introduced.

After a reminder that he can always return and experience good feelings, the counsellor warns the client that he is going to 'wake up' shortly, feeling refreshed and relaxed. She then counts slowly from one to five, describing with each number the process of waking to full alertness.

Clients may sometimes be worried that they have not heard everything, that they drifted off or day-dreamed. They should be reassured that this is just as valuable — and that they will have heard subconsciously everything that the counsellor has said.

Used in some of the ways described, sub-verbal counselling can need confidence and experience but we would urge the counsellor to have the courage to use some of these techniques. She will be surprised at the insight many clients will have in their choices and in the effectiveness of this way of working.

14.

WHY BE A COUNSELLOR?

In this book the authors have attempted to establish that there is a need for counselling that can be recognised in the people with whom we all have contact. Patients and their families will be facing difficulties and problems that inevitably demand adjustment and alteration in their lives and relationships.

All patients?

We would argue, Yes.

Most of us have experienced the extent to which a small injury or disability can affect our lives. A burnt hand, a painful shoulder, a stiff knee, a headache, can affect our ability to function normally to a surprising degree. We can feel frustrated, rejected and unhappy because of the apparent inability of others to appreciate how we are suffering. We may experience guilt or embarrassment about the strength of our negative feelings.

The patients we encounter will mostly be suffering from more acute, more disabling and more long-lasting conditions than the burnt hand or headache that so affected us.

The tests, diagnosis and appropriate treatment will be carried out by relevant staff. The hospital-based social worker and occupational therapist will be involved in any practical problems that may present and are in a position to offer counselling. All too often, however, there seems to be no one to care for the feelings of the patient unless they should become so acutely distressing that psychiatric help is sought. The patient's partner, family and friends are often too affected themselves to offer the creative listening the patient needs. Those close to the patient may be unable to provide the caring support needed for him to come to terms with his problems when their own difficulties are unacknowledged.

A patient may often feel that the doctor or surgeon is too busy to be burdened with what may seem trivial or irrelevant worries. His interviews with medical staff are often focused on symptoms and treatment. He may feel it necessary to be grateful and appreciative. He may see the request for recognition of his disturbing feelings as failure to be grateful and appreciative.

These patients often feel less pressure to conform to their fantasy of 'the good patient' when receiving attention from members of the other caring professions. There seems to be more time allocated to them. Time which is often used in talking about feelings with their therapist or worker.

We do not wish to suggest that there are not members of the medical profession who are not fully aware of their patients' need for counselling, or that there are not some doctors who offer this. However, experience has shown the authors that this is not always the case. Medical practitioners do not always have the time or feel that they are the appropriate people to offer such help. In some cases there is a denial that there is the need for such help.

To the question, 'Why be a counsellor?' we would give a three-fold answer:

1. Someone is in need.
2. Someone has asked me.
3. I want to respond.

RESPONDING

We have already discussed the need, the ways in which someone may ask and what is involved in responding as a counsellor. Why I should want to respond can be discussed in more detail.

To be needed is a very basic human desire.

To feel necessary to another person, to have something to give that another needs, is an affirmation for me. It is an affirmation of my own value, my own worth.

To hear someone say to me, 'It is so easy to talk to you', 'You help me so much', 'No one else could understand', is good. It is always good, however often it is said, however inadequate and unworthy of such praise I sometimes feel. I enjoy being needed and appreciated.

It is sometimes suggested that there is something immoral, degrading, in enjoying the role of counsellor. It seems to be felt that to enjoy appreciation is somehow arrogant or unworthy. We argue very strongly that when the basic need to be needed is met in the counselling relationship it would be unreal and dishonest not to acknowledge and enjoy the good feeling.

Neither is that good feeling unearned. Counselling can be difficult, agonising, frustrating, boring and demanding as well as affirming and rewarding.

The good feelings we get are given to us by our clients and are worth all the difficulties. Sharing and empathising with another human being is humbling, enriching and illuminating.

WHERE DO WE GO FROM HERE?

Having decided that there is a need to which you are willing to respond, and hopefully having responded, what next?

We have indicated very briefly some of the skills that are involved in counselling.

We have discussed the importance of self-awareness and have described a few exercises in self-awareness.

It is obviously impossible to give more than the briefest outline of these. Anyone wishing to develop their own counselling skills will want to go much further.

There is a saying,
'I hear and I forget.
I see and I remember.
I do and I know.'

With this in mind, reading, although very useful, should be regarded as a back-up to experience.

In the bibliography on pages 119–121 the authors suggest a number of books that we have found valuable. These fall into two main categories:

1. Personal accounts of disability and illness. Some are autobiographical, some are written by parents or partners of disabled or ill people. Such accounts are very valuable in reminding us of the feelings of the people with whom we are working, and of the very different reactions of different people. There are also often very salutary accounts of how it feels to be on the receiving end of professional attentions.

2. Those which discuss various models of counselling.

Most counsellors have a variety of 'tools' at their command and will use the model that seems most appropriate to the individual client. Many counsellors have a favourite model that is appropriate to their own philosophy and temperament. That is the model of counselling that they tend to use most often.

We suggest that the student of counselling should study and copy as many models as she can usefully assimilate and experience. Assessment and valuation of the skills used can be carried out with the supervisor.

The opportunity to practise is also available at a number of courses in counselling skills. Courses may be short, offering introduction to specific or general counselling skills or a chance to consolidate learned techniques. Longer courses give experience in specific areas of counselling with full- or part-time courses being available that lead to a qualification in counselling skills. We can give no more than general help in locating courses and would advise prospective counsellors to be as certain as they can of the validity of any course they may select out of the increasing number that are advertised.

Validation is a difficult area. The British Association for Counselling has formulated a validating procedure for counsellors but trainers in counselling do not necessarily have teaching skills as well as counselling skills. Some courses offer only theory and we have already indicated that only experience with supervision and evaluation can increase skill. Some courses describe their approach as a 'workshop experience' when the student group is 40 or more, and a genuine workshop experience when every participant is fully supervised and supported is impossible with such numbers.

Generally speaking, we recommend that courses are sought which are advertised by a recognised college or organisation and that a full description of the course and the tutors concerned is obtained before any commitment is made.

SELECT BIBLIOGRAPHY

Accounts of disability

The following list of books are personal accounts of illness, disability or of living with a person who is ill or disabled. We would recommend reading as many of such accounts as the prospective counsellor is able to find. It is always valuable to gain insight into the world as perceived by another person and, where illness and disability is concerned, our understanding can be enhanced by sensitive reading. Obviously writers vary in sensitivity and insight, and their experiences with various agencies also vary widely. Some salutary comments must be taken to heart by all professionals working in the area of illness and disability.

Jo Campling (ed) (1981) *Images of Ourselves. Women with Disabilities Talking.* Routledge and Kegan Paul, London. A series of personal experiences of being a woman with disability.

Patricia Collins (1981) *Mary: A Mother's Story.* Piatkus Books, London. The early life of a severely cerebral palsied girl and her mother (the author) struggling to accept her child.

James Copeland (1976) *For the Love of Ann.* Arrow Books, London. Experiences of coping with a child with autism before the condition was understood.

Mary Craig (1979) *Blessings.* Coronet Books, London. A mother's account of two sons with severe learning difficulties.

Rosemary Crossley and Anne McDonald (1982) *Annie's Coming Out.* Penguin Books, Harmondsworth. The rescue of a profoundly disabled, highly intelligent girl from a unit for the severely retarded in Australia.

Anne Deveson (1992) *Tell Me I'm Here.* Penguin Books, Harmondsworth. A mother's biography of her schizophrenic son.

Paddy Doyle (1988) *The God Squad.* Corgi Edition, London. The sometimes horrifying autobiography of an institutionalised child in Ireland.

Joseph Heller and Speed Vogel (1987) *No Laughing Matter.* Corgi Edition, London. An irreverent and honest account of Heller's experiences with Guillain-Barré syndrome.

Bronwyn Hocking (1990) *Little Boy Lost.* Bloomsbury Publishing, London. The mother of an autistic boy whose comments on the etiology of the condition and the attitudes of the 'experts' are valuable insights.

Ann Lovell (1979) *Simple Simon.* Lion Publishing, Tring. A contrasting viewpoint to *Little Boy Lost* on the subject of autism.

David Melton (1969) *Todd.* Leslie Frewin. A rare account by the **father** of a boy with brain damage.

Jenny Morris (1989) *Able Lives.* The Women's Press, London. Women's experiences of paralysis.

Nicola Schaefer (1979) *Does She Know She's There?* Futura Publications, London. Bringing up a daughter with severe physical disability and learning difficulties.

A.T. Sutherland (1981) *Disabled We Stand: Human Horizon Series* Souvenir Press, London. Accounts by people with disabilities about the handicaps imposed by society.

Ivan Vaughan (1986) *Ivan. Living with Parkinson's Disease*. Macmillan, London. A very personal account.

Elizabeth Ward (1986) *Timbo: A Struggle for Survival.* Sidgewick and Jackson, London. A remarkable account of the life and death of a boy with kidney disease.

Nicholas Woolley and Sue Clayton (1989) *Just for William.* Penguin Books, Harmondsworth. The life and death of a boy with leukaemia.

Rosemary and Victor Zorza (1980) *A Way to Die: Living to the End.* Andre Deutsch, London. A very open and gut-wrenching yet encouraging account by parents of a daughter's death from melanoma.

General list

Virginia Axline (1964) *Dibs: In Search of Self.* Pelican Books, Harmondsworth. Still the most definitive and moving account of non-directed play therapy in the healing of an emotionally damaged child.

John Bradshaw (1990) *Homecoming.* Piatkus. A clear and accessible explanation of, and exercises to discover, own and champion, our Inner Child.

Gerard Egan (1981) *Skilled Helper: A Systematic Model for Helping.* Brooks/Cole Publishing Co., Pacific Grove, USA.

Helene Frederic and Martine Malinsky (1979) *Martin.* Routledge and Kegan Paul, London. The detailed account of play therapy with a disturbed child.

Sheldon Kopp (1974) *If You Meet the Buddha on the Road — Kill Him! Pilgrimage of Psychotherapy Patients.* Sheldon Press, London. Written by a psychiatrist working with the criminally insane; traditional stories such as the Gilgamesh epic are used to illustrate the psychotherapeutic journey.

Barry Stevens (1981) *Don't Push the River.* Real People Press, Moab, USA. Therapy that allows the client to develop at his own pace— not 'pushing the river' but letting it flow by itself.

Client-centred therapy

Carl Rogers (1965) *Client Centred Therapy.* Constable, London.

Carl Rogers (1974) *On Becoming a Person.* Constable, London.

Death

Ian Chrichton (1976) *The Art of Dying.* Owen (Peter) Ltd, London.

Gestalt therapy

Fredrick S. Perls, *et al.* (1981) *Gestalt Therapy Verbatim.* Real People Press, Moab, USA.

Transactional analysis

Eric Berne (1970) *Games People Play: Psychology of Human Relationships.* Penguin Books, Harmondsworth.

Thomas A. Harris (1973) *I'm OK — You're OK.* Pan Books, London.

Sexuality and disability

Michael Craft and Ann Craft (1982) *Sex and the Mentally Handicapped: A Guide for Parents and Carers.* Routledge and Kegan Paul, London.

Bernadette Fallon (1976) *So You're Paralysed.* Spinal Injuries Association, London.

Heslinga, K. (1977) *Not Made of Stone: Sexual Problems of Handicapped People.* Woodhead-Faulkner, Cambridge.

Stewart, W.R.F. (1975) *Sex and the Physically Handicapped.* National Foundation for Research into Crippling Disease, Horsham, Sussex.

Stewart, W.R.F. (1979) *Sexual Aspects of Social Work.* Woodhead-Faulkner, Cambridge.

Stewart, W.R.F. (1979) *The Sexual Side of Handicap: Guide for the Caring Professions.* Woodhead-Faulkner, Cambridge.

USEFUL ORGANISATIONS

Of necessity this is a select list of organisations and agencies which can offer help, advice and counselling. A useful guide book for extensive information about many organisations is the Directory for the Disabled edited by A. Darnborough and D. Kinrade and published by Woodhead-Faulkner, Cambridge CB2 3PF. It is updated regularly, and is available in the reference department of most public libraries.

British Association for Counselling
1 Regent Place, Rugby, Warwickshire CV21 2PJ
BAC run short courses in counselling and advertise others in their bulletins and news-sheets. These include articles and book reviews.

Family Planning Association
27-35 Mortimer Street, London W1H 7RJ
The FPA run short courses in counselling skills. Resource lists and reading lists are published. A bookshop in Mortimer Street stocks an extensive range of relevant literature.

RELATE
Herbert Gray College, Little Church Street, Rugby, Warwickshire CV21 3AP
Counselling can be obtained at local centres, and courses are organised in a number of areas.

SPOD (Association to Aid Sexual and Personal Relationships of the Disabled)
286 Camden Road, London N7 0BJ
SPOD run short courses in counselling in the area of disability. Resource lists and reading lists are published. The bulletins contain articles and reviews of relevant literature. Advice is given and in some instances referral can be made to approved counsellors. A library of books and resources is available.

Royal Association for Disability and Rehabilitation (RADAR)
250 City Road, London, EC1V 8AS
RADAR is a co-ordinating and information disseminating organisation for voluntary groups involved in disability. There are a number of publications and bulletins.

The Samaritans
10 The Grove, Slough, SL1 1PQ

The Carers National Association
22–25 Glasshouse Yard, London, EC1A 4JS

INDEX